LINEAR EQUATIONS

BY

P. M. COHN

LONDON: Routledge & Kegan Paul Ltd

KT-366-050

First published 1958
in Great Britain by
Routledge & Kegan Paul Limited
Broadway House, 68–74 Carter Lane
London EC4V 5EL

Reprinted 1959, 1961, 1962, 1964, 1967 and 1971

No part of this book may be reproduced in any form without permission from the publisher, except for the quotation of brief passages in criticism

© *P. M. Cohn 1958*

ISBN 0 7100 6181 1

Printed in Great Britain
by Butler & Tanner Limited
Frome and London

Preface

LINEAR equations play an important part, not only in mathematics itself, but also in many fields in which mathematics is used. Whether we deal with elastic deformations or electrical networks, the flutter of aeroplane wings or the estimation of errors by the method of least squares, at some stage in the calculation we encounter a system of linear equations. In each case the problem of solving the equations is the same, and it is with the mathematical treatment of this question that this book is concerned. By meeting the problem in its pure state the reader will gain an insight which it is hoped will help him when he comes to apply it to his field of work. The actual process of setting up the equations and of interpreting the solution is one which more properly belongs to that field, and in any case is a problem of a different nature altogether. So we need not concern ourselves with it here and are able to concentrate on the mathematical aspect of the situation.

The most important tools for handling linear equations are vectors and matrices, and their basic properties are developed in separate chapters. The method by which the nature of the solution is described is one which leads immediately to a solution in practical cases, and it is a method frequently adopted when solving problems by mechanical or electronic computers. Determinants are not used at all in this process, but as they occur in many applications and lead to practical criteria, a chapter on the properties of determinants has been included.

No specific knowledge is presupposed, although a slight acquaintance with plane coordinate geometry will lighten the reader's task. It is necessary, however, to remark that the book is not merely intended as a reference book of useful formulae. Rather it is addressed to the student who wants to gain an understanding of the subject. With this end in mind, the exposition has been limited to basic notions, explained as fully as possible, with detailed proofs. Some of the proofs may be omitted at first, but they do form an integral part of the treatment and, it is hoped, will help the reader to grasp the underlying principles.

I should like to record the great debt I owe to the editor, Dr. Walter Ledermann, for the discussions I have had with him, and for his very constructive criticism of the manuscript. In addition the manuscript has been read by my colleagues, Dr. J. A. Green and Dr. H. Ruben, and I should like to express my thanks to them here for their helpful suggestions.

P. M. COHN

The University,
Manchester

Contents

Introduction

To solve a system of linear equations means to find all the values of the unknowns which satisfy the equations. For problems with two or three unknowns this is not difficult, but when there are more unknowns a systematic method is needed. And even with a few unknowns there are several possibilities which have to be taken into account.

The simplest type of system is that of one equation in one unknown:

$$ax=k. \tag{1}$$

Everyone will recognize the solution of this equation to be $x=\frac{k}{a}$, but that is true only when $a\neq 0$. To be quite precise, we have to distinguish two cases:

(i) $a\neq 0$. Then there is exactly one value of x satisfying (1), namely $x=\frac{k}{a}$.

(ii) $a=0$. In this case no value of x satisfies (1) if $k\neq 0$, but if $k=0$, every value of x satisfies (1).

This distinction is fundamental in all that follows. For when we try to solve a system of several equations in several unknowns,[1] the process of solution may be more complicated, but there are again two cases corresponding to (i) and (ii), with a subdivision of case (ii) according to the value of the right-hand sides of the equations.

The following examples illustrate this in the case of two equations in two unknowns. Consider the equations

$$\begin{aligned} 3x+2y&=7\\ 2x+5y&=12. \end{aligned} \tag{2}$$

If there exist x and y satisfying both these equations, then by

[1] The number of unknowns need not be the same as the number of equations.

eliminating y and x in turn we find

$$(5.3-2.2)x=5.7-2.12$$
$$(2.2-3.5)y=2.7-3.12,$$

which simplifies to $x=1$, $y=2$. So this is the only pair of values which can satisfy (2), and it does in fact satisfy (2), as is easily verified. We see that there is exactly one set of values of x and y satisfying (2), or as we shall say, the equations (2) have a *unique solution.*

The same method applied to the system

$$\begin{aligned} 3x+2y&=7 \\ 6x+4y&=11, \end{aligned} \qquad (3)$$

gives

$$(4.3-2.6)x=4.7-2.11$$
$$(6.2-3.4)y=6.7-3.11;$$

here the left-hand sides are zero whatever the values of x and y, but the right-hand sides are not zero. We conclude that (3) has no solution, a fact which we could have found directly by observing that the left-hand side of the second equation in (3) is twice the left-hand side of the first, so that the equations can only have a solution if the same relation holds between the right-hand sides. In the system

$$\begin{aligned} 3x+2y&=7 \\ 6x+4y&=14, \end{aligned} \qquad (4)$$

this is the case, in fact the second equation is just twice the first equation and therefore any values of x and y satisfying the first equation of (4) form a solution of (4). There are infinitely many such solutions: if we assign an arbitrary value, say λ, to x, then there is just one solution of (4) with this value for x, namely

$$\begin{aligned} x&=\lambda \\ y&=\tfrac{1}{2}(7-3\lambda). \end{aligned} \qquad (5)$$

This solution, involving the parameter λ, is the *complete* solution of (4) in the sense that we get all the different solutions of (4) by assigning all possible numerical values to λ in (5).

If we interpret x and y as rectangular coordinates in the plane then a linear equation in x and y is represented by a straight line, and the solution of a system of two such equations corresponds to the intersections of the straight lines representing the equations. Let us draw these lines for each of the

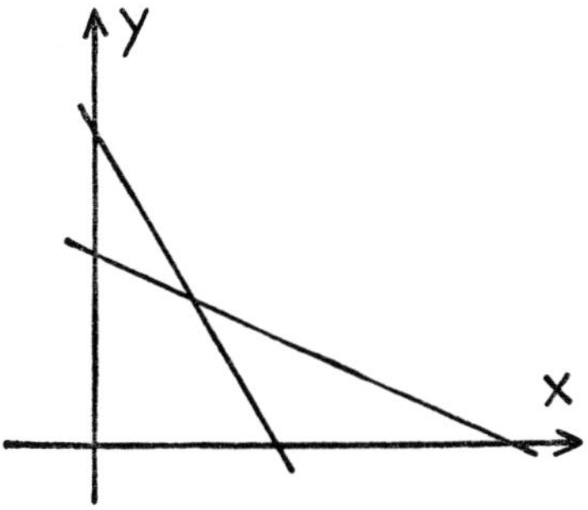

FIG. 1.

systems (2), (3), (4). In the first case we have two lines intersecting in a single point (Fig. 1), corresponding to the unique solution of (2). The system (3), which has no solution, corresponds to two parallel lines (Fig. 2), and (4), which has an

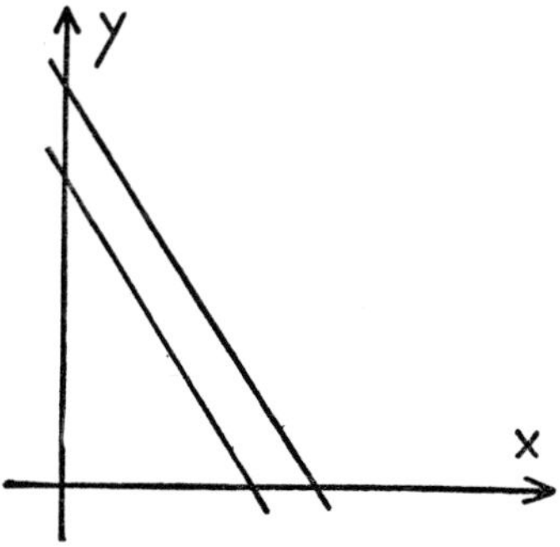

FIG. 2.

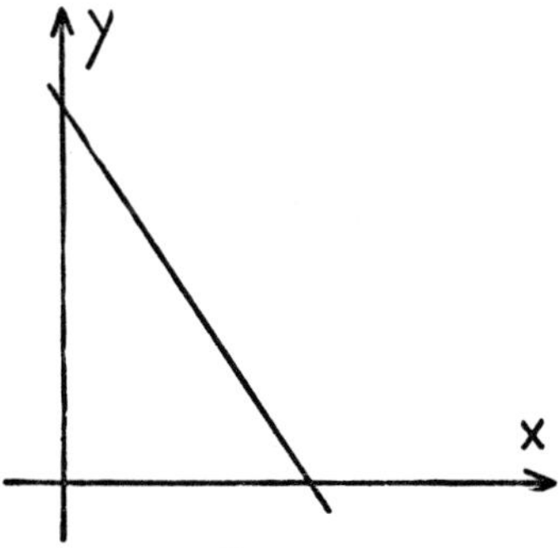

FIG. 3.

infinity of solutions, corresponds to two coincident lines (Fig. 3): here the 'intersection' is the whole line.

Our aim is to give a method of finding the complete solution of a given system of linear equations (when a solution exists), which is sufficiently systematic to be applied to any number of equations in any number of unknowns. While the actual process used is not much more than the familiar elimination of the unknowns, the point of view emphasizes the relation of the general problem to the simplest case (1). Corresponding to the types (i) and (ii) of the system (1) we shall distinguish two cases and deal with the case of the 'regular' system before taking the general case.

CHAPTER ONE

Vectors

1. The systems we met in the Introduction consisted of two equations in two unknowns. In the general case we have a system of m equations in n unknowns,[1] briefly, an $m \times n$ system.

$$\begin{aligned} a_{11}x_1+a_{12}x_2+\ \ldots\ +a_{1n}x_n&=k_1\\ a_{21}x_1+a_{22}x_2+\ \ldots\ +a_{2n}x_n&=k_2\\ \ldots\qquad \ldots\qquad &\ldots\\ a_{m1}x_1+a_{m2}x_2+\ \ldots\ +a_{mn}x_n&=k_m. \end{aligned} \tag{1}$$

The a's and k's are given numbers[2] and we require all n-tuples of numbers $(x_1, x_2, \ldots, x_n)$ satisfying the equations. When we consider a particular instance of (1), in which the a's and k's have particular numerical values, the equations must of course be written out in full, but as long as we are dealing with the general system, we can abbreviate it in various ways. Thus we can write (1) as

$$a_{i1}x_1+a_{i2}x_2+\ \ldots\ +a_{in}x_n=k_i \quad (i=1, \ldots, m). \tag{2}$$

When we give i the values 1, 2, . . . , m in succession we just get (1). The sum on the left of (2) is sometimes abbreviated by writing down the general term, say the j-th term, of this sum: $a_{ij}x_j$, and placing a Σ on the left (to indicate summation) with some indication of the range of j. Thus (2) may be written as

$$\sum_{j=1}^{n} a_{ij}x_j=k_i \qquad (i=1, \ldots, m), \tag{3}$$

[1] The case where some of the equations do not involve all the unknowns is covered by allowing the coefficients to be zero.

[2] We shall always assume that the coefficients are real numbers, but everything that is said applies if complex numbers are used. In practice the coefficients (and solutions) are often only known approximately and are given as decimal fractions. However this makes no difference of principle, and in our examples we shall give quite simple values to the coefficients so as not to obscure the argument.

or simply $\sum_j a_{ij}x_j=k_i$, when the ranges of i and j are clear from the context.

2. By a *vector* we shall understand a row of numbers $(x_1, x_2, \ldots, x_n)$. Vectors will usually be denoted by small letters in heavy type, thus we may write $\mathbf{x}=(x_1, \ldots, x_n)$. The numbers $x_1, \ldots, x_n$ are called the *components* or *coordinates* of $\mathbf{x}$; the integer n is called its *dimension*, we also call $\mathbf{x}$ an n-vector. In contradistinction to a vector, a number is called a *scalar*.[1]

The dimension n can have any value 1, 2, 3, ... The 1-vectors are the simplest case of vectors, though perhaps a rather trivial one. The 2-vectors are pairs of numbers: $\mathbf{x}=(x_1, x_2)$. If with the vector (x_1, x_2) we associate the point P of the plane whose coordinates in a given coordinate system are x_1, x_2, we establish a correspondence between 2-vectors and points of the plane[2] which will enable us to interpret our results geometrically, at least for dimension 2. In a similar way the 3-vectors can be represented by the points of space; for $n>3$ there is no such intuitive picture to help us, but there is no difference in principle between 3-vectors and n-vectors for $n>3$.

The order of the components in a vector is essential. E.g. $(3, 7, -1)\neq(7, 3, -1)$, and generally, two vectors are equal:

$$(x_1, \ldots, x_n)=(y_1, \ldots, y_n), \tag{4}$$

if and only if corresponding components are equal:

$$x_i=y_i \qquad (i=1, \ldots, n).$$

Thus any equation between n-vectors is equivalent to n scalar equations; we express this fact by saying that we may equate the components in equation (4).

3. If vectors are to serve our purpose of describing the system (1), we must know how to add them and multiply them by

[1] In physics entities like displacements, velocities or forces may be represented by vectors, whence the origin of the word 'vector' (literally: 'carrier'). Numerical quantities such as temperatures, lengths, speeds or weights are called 'scalars' because they may be read off on a scale.

[2] As in the illustrations given in the Introduction.

scalars. In defining these operations we shall suppose that the dimension, though arbitrary, is the same for all vectors considered; we denote it by n. The reader may find it helpful at first to keep in mind a definite case, say $n=3$.

Given two vectors $\mathbf{x}=(x_1, \ldots, x_n)$ and $\mathbf{y}=(y_1, \ldots, y_n)$, the vector

$$(x_1+y_1, \ldots, x_n+y_n)$$

is called the *sum* of $\mathbf{x}$ and $\mathbf{y}$ and is denoted by $\mathbf{x}+\mathbf{y}$. E.g. $(3, 7, -4)+(2, -1, 0)=(5, 6, -4)$. The particular vector whose components are all zero is called the *zero-vector* and is denoted by $\mathbf{0}$, thus $\mathbf{0}=(0, 0, \ldots, 0)$.

The addition of numbers satisfies certain laws, and it turns out that these laws also hold for the addition of vectors. We list them here, but do not give a proof as they are all easily deduced from the corresponding laws of numbers by equating components.

V.1. $\mathbf{x}+\mathbf{y}=\mathbf{y}+\mathbf{x}$ (commutative law of addition),

V.2. $(\mathbf{x}+\mathbf{y})+\mathbf{z}=\mathbf{x}+(\mathbf{y}+\mathbf{z})$ (associative law of addition),

V.3. $\mathbf{x}+\mathbf{0}=\mathbf{x}$,

V.4. *For each vector* $\mathbf{x}$ *there is a vector* $-\mathbf{x}$ *such that*

$$\mathbf{x}+(-\mathbf{x})=\mathbf{0}.$$

In V.4, if $\mathbf{x}=(x_1, \ldots, x_n)$, then $-\mathbf{x}=(-x_1, \ldots, -x_n)$, which accounts for the choice of the notation $-\mathbf{x}$.

4. If $\mathbf{x}=(x_1, \ldots, x_n)$ and λ is a scalar, we define a new vector $\lambda\mathbf{x}$ or $\mathbf{x}\lambda$ by the equation

$$\lambda\mathbf{x}=(\lambda x_1, \ldots, \lambda x_n).$$

This vector $\lambda\mathbf{x}$ which may be called the *product* of the scalar λ by the vector $\mathbf{x}$, satisfies the rules

V.5. $\lambda(\mathbf{x}+\mathbf{y})=\lambda\mathbf{x}+\lambda\mathbf{y}$,
V.6. $(\lambda+\mu)\mathbf{x}=\lambda\mathbf{x}+\mu\mathbf{x}$, (distributive laws)

V.7. $(\lambda\mu)\mathbf{x}=\lambda(\mu\mathbf{x})$,

V.8. $1\mathbf{x}=\mathbf{x}$,

V.9. $0\mathbf{x}=\mathbf{0}$,

where $\mathbf{x}$ and $\mathbf{y}$ are any vectors and λ, μ any scalars. In V.9 we note that the scalar zero 0 appears on the left, while on the right we have the zero-vector $\mathbf{0}$. These laws can again be verified by equating components.

From the definitions we see that $(-1)\mathbf{x}$ equals $-\mathbf{x}$, as defined after V.4; we shall simply write $-\lambda\mathbf{x}$ for $(-\lambda)\mathbf{x}$ and $\mathbf{x}-\mathbf{y}$ instead of $\mathbf{x}+(-\mathbf{y})$.

The set of all vectors of dimension n with these rules of addition and multiplication by scalars is called the *space* of all n-vectors or the *vector space* of dimension n.

5. All that has been said can be interpreted geometrically when $n=2$ or 3. Thus the zero-vector $\mathbf{0}$ represents the origin O, and if the non-zero vectors $\mathbf{x}$ and $\mathbf{y}$ correspond to the points P and Q respectively, then their sum $\mathbf{x}+\mathbf{y}$ corresponds to the point R which is the fourth vertex of the parallelogram with sides OP and OQ. Any

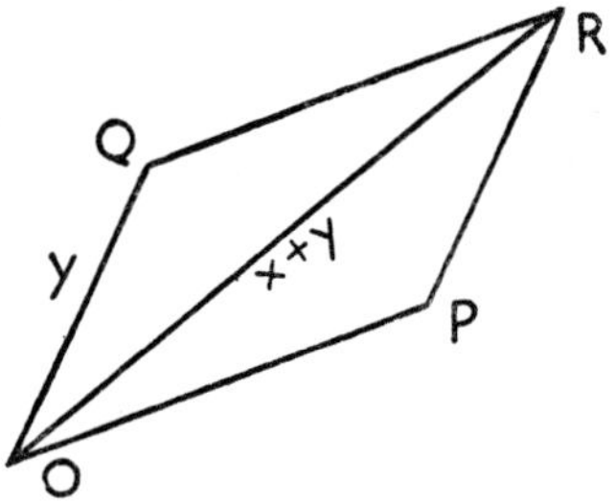

FIG. 4.

scalar multiple $\lambda\mathbf{x}$ of $\mathbf{x}$ represents a point on the line OP, produced in both directions, and all the points of this line are represented by scalar multiples of $\mathbf{x}$.

We note that the point R in Fig. 4 lies in a plane with the points OPQ, even if $\mathbf{x}$ and $\mathbf{y}$ are vectors in three dimensions. More generally, the vector

$$\mathbf{z}=\lambda\mathbf{x}+\mu\mathbf{y},$$

where λ and μ are any scalars, again lies in a plane with $\mathbf{x}$ and $\mathbf{y}$. We call such a vector $\mathbf{z}$ a *linear combination* of $\mathbf{x}$ and $\mathbf{y}$, and we say: $\mathbf{z}$ *depends linearly* on $\mathbf{x}$ and $\mathbf{y}$.

Generally, a vector $\mathbf{z}$ is said to depend linearly on the vectors $\mathbf{u}_1, \ldots, \mathbf{u}_k$, if there are scalars $\lambda_1, \ldots, \lambda_k$ such that

$$\mathbf{z}=\lambda_1\mathbf{u}_1+\ldots+\lambda_k\mathbf{u}_k \qquad (5)$$

E.g., (4, 6, 2) depends linearly on the vectors (2, 0, −2), (−1, 3, 4): (4, 6, 2) = 3(2, 0, −2) + 2(−1, 3, 4).

6. A set of vectors $\mathbf{u}_1, \ldots, \mathbf{u}_k$ is called *linearly dependent*, if one of these vectors depends linearly on the rest, say if

$$\mathbf{u}_1 = \lambda_2\mathbf{u}_2 + \ldots + \lambda_k\mathbf{u}_k.$$

If the vectors $\mathbf{u}_1, \ldots, \mathbf{u}_k$ are not linearly dependent, i.e. if none of the vectors can be expressed linearly in terms of the remaining ones, we say that the vectors are *linearly independent*.

The definition of linear dependence can be expressed in a slightly different, more symmetric form as follows:

The vectors $\mathbf{u}_1, \ldots, \mathbf{u}_k$ *are linearly dependent if and only if there is a relation*

$$\alpha_1\mathbf{u}_1 + \alpha_2\mathbf{u}_2 + \ldots + \alpha_k\mathbf{u}_k = \mathbf{0},$$

in which the scalars α_i *are not all zero.*

For if the vectors are linearly dependent, say if

$$\mathbf{u}_1 = \lambda_2\mathbf{u}_2 + \ldots + \lambda_k\mathbf{u}_k,$$

then

$$\mathbf{u}_1 - \lambda_2\mathbf{u}_2 - \ldots - \lambda_k\mathbf{u}_k = \mathbf{0},$$

and this is a non-trivial relation between the **u**'s—i.e. one in which the coefficients are not all zero—because the coefficient of $\mathbf{u}_1$ is 1. Conversely, if there is a relation

$$\alpha_1\mathbf{u}_1 + \alpha_2\mathbf{u}_2 + \ldots + \alpha_k\mathbf{u}_k = \mathbf{0}$$

in which the α_i are not all zero, say $\alpha_1 \neq 0$, then

$$\mathbf{u}_1 = \beta_2\mathbf{u}_2 + \ldots + \beta_k\mathbf{u}_k,$$

where $\beta_i = -\alpha_i/\alpha_1$ $(i = 2, \ldots, k)$; this shows that the vectors are linearly dependent.

Illustration: The vectors $\mathbf{u} = (2, 3, 1)$, $\mathbf{v} = (2, 0, -2)$, $\mathbf{w} = (-1, 3, 4)$ are linearly dependent, for $2\mathbf{u} - 3\mathbf{v} - 2\mathbf{w} = \mathbf{0}$, and hence $\mathbf{u} = (3/2)\mathbf{v} + \mathbf{w}$.

The second form of the dependence condition is often more convenient. It shows that a set of vectors is linearly independent, if and only if the only linear relation between the vectors is the *trivial* one, in which all the coefficients are zero. A set consisting of a single vector **u** is linearly dependent if and only if there is a relation $\alpha\mathbf{u}=\mathbf{0}$ with $\alpha\neq 0$, which is true precisely when $\mathbf{u}=\mathbf{0}$. Generally any set which includes the zero-vector is linearly dependent, for the set $\mathbf{0}, \mathbf{u}_1, \ldots, \mathbf{u}_k$ satisfies the relation

$$1\cdot\mathbf{0}+0\cdot\mathbf{u}_1+\ldots+0\cdot\mathbf{u}_k=\mathbf{0},$$

in which not all the coefficients are zero.

7. In general, if a vector $\mathbf{z}$ depends linearly on the vectors $\mathbf{u}_1, \ldots, \mathbf{u}_k$, there are different ways of expressing this dependence. For if

$$\mathbf{z}=\lambda_1\mathbf{u}_1+\ldots+\lambda_k\mathbf{u}_k, \tag{5}$$

and if

$$\alpha_1\mathbf{u}_1+\ldots+\alpha_k\mathbf{u}_k=\mathbf{0} \tag{6}$$

is any linear relation between the $\mathbf{u}$'s, then we also have

$$\mathbf{z}=(\lambda_1+\alpha_1)\mathbf{u}_1+\ldots+(\lambda_k+\alpha_k)\mathbf{u}_k, \tag{7}$$

and this expression for $\mathbf{z}$ is different from the expression in (5) unless all the α_i are zero. Therefore, if $\mathbf{u}_1, \ldots, \mathbf{u}_k$ are linearly dependent, there are different ways of expressing $\mathbf{z}$ linearly in terms of the $\mathbf{u}_i$.

On the other hand, if $\mathbf{u}_1, \ldots, \mathbf{u}_k$ are linearly independent, then the expression (5) for $\mathbf{z}$ is unique. For if

$$\mathbf{z}=\mu_1\mathbf{u}_1+\ldots+\mu_k\mathbf{u}_k \tag{8}$$

is another way of expressing $\mathbf{z}$ in terms of the $\mathbf{u}$'s, then by subtracting (8) from (5), we obtain

$$(\lambda_1-\mu_1)\mathbf{u}_1+\ldots+(\lambda_k-\mu_k)\mathbf{u}_k=\mathbf{0}.$$

Since $\mathbf{u}_1, \ldots, \mathbf{u}_k$ are linearly independent, the coefficients in this relation must all be zero, i.e.

$$\lambda_i=\mu_i \qquad (i=1, \ldots, k),$$

and so (8) is really the same expression as (5). This result may also be expressed as follows:

In the expression (5) *for* $\mathbf{z}$ *the coefficients* λ_i *are uniquely determined by* $\mathbf{z}$ *if and only if the vectors* $\mathbf{u}_1, \ldots, \mathbf{u}_k$ *are linearly independent.*

8. Let us write $\mathbf{e}_i$ for the n-vector whose i-th component is 1

and whose other components are 0; thus $\mathbf{e}_1=(1, 0, \ldots, 0)$, $\mathbf{e}_2=(0, 1, 0, \ldots, 0)$, etc. Every vector of dimension n depends linearly on $\mathbf{e}_1, \mathbf{e}_2, \ldots, \mathbf{e}_n$: if $\mathbf{x}=(x_1, \ldots, x_n)$, then

$$\mathbf{x}=x_1\mathbf{e}_1+\ldots+x_n\mathbf{e}_n. \tag{9}$$

We express this fact by saying that the $\mathbf{e}_i$ *span* the space of all n-vectors. The coefficients in (9) are uniquely determined as the components of $\mathbf{x}$, hence the $\mathbf{e}_i$ are linearly independent. Any set of linearly independent vectors which spans the space of all n-vectors is called a *basis* of that space. We shall frequently use the basis $\mathbf{e}_1, \ldots, \mathbf{e}_n$ introduced above; in the geometrical picture for $n=3$ the $\mathbf{e}_i$ represent points at unit distance along the coordinate axes, and equation (9) states then that every vector can be written as a linear combination of vectors along the axes.

Of course there are many other bases of the same space; an example is the set $(1, 0, 0, \ldots, 0)$, $(1, 1, 0, \ldots, 0)$, $\ldots$, $(1, 1, \ldots, 1)$, in which the i-th vector consists of i ones followed by $n-i$ zeros. In the next chapter we shall see that every basis of the space has exactly n elements.

9. Suppose that we are given k linearly independent vectors $\mathbf{u}_1, \ldots, \mathbf{u}_k$; then every vector $\mathbf{x}$ which depends[1] on the $\mathbf{u}_i$ can be uniquely written as

$$\mathbf{x}=\xi_1\mathbf{u}_1+\ldots+\xi_k\mathbf{u}_k. \tag{10}$$

If $\mathbf{y}=\sum_i \eta_i\mathbf{u}_i$ is another vector depending[1] on the $\mathbf{u}_i$, then it follows from V.6 and V.7 that

$$\mathbf{x}+\mathbf{y}=\sum_i(\xi_i+\eta_i)\mathbf{u}_i, \quad \lambda\mathbf{x}=\sum_i(\lambda\xi_i)\mathbf{u}_i.$$

These formulae show that we may regard the set of all vectors dependent on $\mathbf{u}_1, \ldots, \mathbf{u}_k$ as a vector space of dimension k, by taking $\xi_1, \ldots, \xi_k$, given by (10), to be the components of $\mathbf{x}$. Clearly the vectors $\mathbf{u}_1, \ldots, \mathbf{u}_k$ form a basis of this space.[2]

[1] The word 'linear(ly)' is sometimes omitted, when there is no risk of ambiguity.

[2] At this stage the dimension of a space seems not to be a unique integer, but to depend on the choice of a basis for the space. We shall find in ch. II that this dependence is only apparent.

As an illustration consider two linearly independent vectors $\mathbf{u}$, $\mathbf{v}$ in 3-dimensional space, represented by the points P, Q respectively. To say that $\mathbf{u}$ and $\mathbf{v}$ are linearly independent means that neither is a multiple of the other; it follows that P and Q are not collinear with the origin and so determine a plane. Any point R of this plane corresponds to a vector $\lambda\mathbf{u}+\mu\mathbf{v}$, where λ and μ are uniquely determined by R. Thus the plane may be regarded as a 2-dimensional space with co-ordinates λ, μ.

Suppose now that $\mathbf{u}_1, \ldots, \mathbf{u}_m$ are any set of n-vectors, dependent or not. Then we can still define the space spanned by $\mathbf{u}_1, \ldots, \mathbf{u}_m$ as the set of all vectors dependent on $\mathbf{u}_1, \ldots, \mathbf{u}_m$; to obtain a basis of this space we proceed as follows: if $\mathbf{u}_1, \ldots, \mathbf{u}_m$ are linearly independent, then they form a basis by what has been said. If they are dependent, then one of the vectors, say, $\mathbf{u}_m$, depends on the rest and in this case $\mathbf{u}_1, \ldots, \mathbf{u}_{m-1}$ already span the space. If these vectors are still dependent, we can again express one of them in terms of the rest and so reduce their number by one. In this way we finally obtain a linearly independent set spanning the space, which by definition is a basis of the space, unless all the $\mathbf{u}_i$ were zero. In that case the space consists only of the zero-vector.[1]

EXERCISES ON CHAPTER I

1. Write the following expressions out in full:

$$\sum_{i=1}^{3} a_i b_i, \quad \sum_{j=1}^{2} a_{ij} x_j, \quad \sum_{j=1}^{2} a_{ij} b_{jk}, \quad \sum_{i=1}^{2} \sum_{j=1}^{2} u_i b_{ij} x_j, \quad \sum_{j=1}^{2} \sum_{i=1}^{2} u_i b_{ij} x_j.$$

2. Which of the following sets are linearly dependent?

(i) (0, 1, 1), (1, 0, 1), (1, 1, 0),
(ii) (1, 2, 3), (4, 5, 6), (7, 8, 9),
(iii) (13, 7, 9, 2), (0, 0, 0, 0), (3, −2, 5, 8),
(iv) (4, 0, 3, 2), (2, 1, −1, 3), (−2, −3, 6, −7).

[1] Formally this may be regarded as the 0-dimensional space, with a basis of zero elements.

3. Show that the following set is linearly dependent, although the first vector does not depend on the remaining two:

$$(16, 12, 15, -10), (9, -15, -6, 24), (-15, 25, 10, -40).$$

4. How can the statement that two 3-vectors are linearly independent be interpreted geometrically?

5. Show that the vectors $(2, -1, 0, 0)$, $(1, 1, 1, 1)$, $(-1, 1, 1, -1)$, $(0, 0, 1, 3)$ span the space of all 4-vectors.

6. Show that the vectors (x_1, x_2, x_3, x_4) satisfying the conditions $x_1=0$, $x_3=x_4$, form a vector space, by finding a basis for this space.

7. Show that the polynomials in a single variable x of degree at most 3 can be regarded as a vector space, with the basis $1, x, x^2, x^3$. (Ignore the multiplication of polynomials, and take as the 'coordinates' of a polynomial its coefficients.)

CHAPTER TWO

The Solution of a System of Equations: the Regular Case

1. With the help of vector notation any $m \times n$ system may be written as a single vector equation. E.g. the 2×2 system

$$\begin{aligned} 3x+2y&=7 \\ 2x+5y&=12, \end{aligned}$$

considered in the Introduction, may be written as

$$\begin{pmatrix} 3 \\ 2 \end{pmatrix} x + \begin{pmatrix} 2 \\ 5 \end{pmatrix} y = \begin{pmatrix} 7 \\ 12 \end{pmatrix}$$

where the vectors have been written as columns, instead of rows as in ch. I. This way of writing the equations puts the problem in a different light. To solve this vector equation is to express the vector on the right as a linear combination of the two vectors on the left.

We can treat the general $m \times n$ system

$$\begin{aligned} a_{11}x_1 + \dots + a_{1n}x_n &= k_1 \\ \cdot \quad \cdot \quad \cdots \quad \cdots & \\ a_{m1}x_1 + \dots + a_{mn}x_n &= k_m \end{aligned} \tag{1}$$

similarly. Let us write

$$\mathbf{a}_j = \begin{pmatrix} a_{1j} \\ \cdot \\ \cdot \\ \cdot \\ a_{mj} \end{pmatrix} \qquad (j=1, \dots, n),$$

and call $\mathbf{a}_1, \dots, \mathbf{a}_n$ the *column-vectors*, or simply the *columns*, of the system (1). In order to save space we often write the components of a column-vector in a horizontal row, with a dash to show that it is really a column.[1] Thus the definition of $\mathbf{a}_j$ may be written

$$\mathbf{a}_j=(a_{1j}, \ldots, a_{mj})' \qquad (j=1, \ldots, n).$$

If we put $\mathbf{k}=(k_1, \ldots, k_m)'$, then (1) may be written as a vector equation

$$\mathbf{a}_1x_1+ \ldots +\mathbf{a}_nx_n=\mathbf{k}. \tag{2}$$

The problem is to determine the possible sets of values for the x_i, that is, the possible ways of expressing $\mathbf{k}$ as a linear combination of $\mathbf{a}_1, \ldots, \mathbf{a}_n$.

In this chapter we shall consider a specially important case of the system (1), namely the case where $m=n$ and the n columns on the left of (1) are linearly independent. Such a system will be called a *regular* system of *order n*. Our aim will be to prove

Theorem 1. *A regular system of equations has exactly one solution.*

2. Before proving Theorem 1 we remark firstly, that whether a given $n\times n$ system is regular or not depends only on the coefficients a_{ij} on the left-hand side, not on the coefficients k_i on the right, so that if a given system is regular, it has a solution for every value of the right-hand side.

Secondly, to say that the system (2) is regular is to say that the vectors $\mathbf{a}_1, \ldots, \mathbf{a}_n$ are n-dimensional, and are linearly independent. This means that there is no non-trivial relation between them; we can therefore restate Theorem 1 as

Theorem 1′. *If* $\mathbf{a}_1, \ldots, \mathbf{a}_n$ *are any n vectors (of dimension n) such that*

$$\mathbf{a}_1x_1+ \ldots \mathbf{a}_nx_n=\mathbf{0}$$

has only the trivial solution $(x_1, \ldots, x_n)=(0, \ldots, 0)$, *then the system*

$$\mathbf{a}_1x_1+ \ldots +\mathbf{a}_nx_n=\mathbf{k}$$

has, for any vector $\mathbf{k}$, *just one solution* $(x_1, \ldots, x_n)$.

[1] We stress the fact that these vectors are columns in view of later developments, when it becomes necessary to distinguish them from vectors which are expressed as rows.

3. The proof of Theorem 1, which will at the same time give a practical method of solving the equations, amounts to showing that the traditional process of eliminating the variables one by one can be carried out. This process of elimination consists in adding multiples of one equation to another. In other words, we have to modify the system of equations in a way which does not affect the solutions. All such ways of operating on a system can be obtained as a succession of the following 'elementary' operations:

α. *Writing the same equations in a different order,*

β. *multiplying an equation by a non-zero scalar,*

γ. *adding a multiple of one equation to another equation of the system.*

Let us say that two systems of equations in the same unknowns $x_1, \ldots, x_n$ are *equivalent*, if they each contain the same number of equations and have the same solutions. We shall show that the operations α, β, γ, applied to any system, produce an equivalent system.

This is clear for the operation α, for it simply amounts to renumbering the equations. To show that β and γ yield equivalent systems, let us abbreviate the i-th equation by writing

$$f_i(\mathbf{x})=a_{i1}x_1+\ldots+a_{in}x_n-k_n \qquad (i=1, \ldots, n).$$

If $\mathbf{u}$ is a solution of the original equations, then

$$f_1(\mathbf{u})=f_2(\mathbf{u})=\ldots=f_n(\mathbf{u})=0. \tag{3}$$

Now apply β, say by multiplying the first equation by λ, where $\lambda\neq 0$. Clearly

$$\lambda f_1(\mathbf{u})=f_2(\mathbf{u})=\ldots=f_n(\mathbf{u})=0, \tag{4}$$

which shows that $\mathbf{u}$ satisfies the new equations. Conversely, if (4) holds then on dividing the first equation by λ—which we may do because $\lambda\neq 0$—we obtain (3), so that every solution of the new system also satisfies the original system. Similarly, if (3) holds, and we apply γ, say by replacing the left-hand side of the first equation by $f_1(\mathbf{x})+\mu f_2(\mathbf{x})$, then we have, by (3),

$$f_1(\mathbf{u})+\mu f_2(\mathbf{u})=f_2(\mathbf{u})=f_3(\mathbf{u})=\ldots=f_n(\mathbf{u})=0, \tag{5}$$

and conversely, when (5) holds we can get back to (3) by subtracting μf_2 from $f_1+\mu f_2$. The same reasoning applies when the operations involve equations other than the first and second, and it is clear that the number of equations remains unchanged. Thus we obtain an equivalent system by the application of any of the operations α, β, γ.

This argument does not make use of the regularity of the system, so that it applies to any $m \times n$ system.

4. As we are only concerned with finding the solutions of our system, we may apply the operations α, β, γ which we saw do not affect the solutions. But we have to show also that they do not affect the property of being regular. To say that the original system is regular is to say that when the vector on the right-hand side is $\mathbf{0}$, the system has only the trivial solution (see No. 2). Applying one of α, β, γ to such a system, we again get $\mathbf{0}$ on the right, and since the new system is equivalent to the old, it has again only the trivial solution. Moreover, the number of equations or unknowns has not been changed by these operations, therefore the new system is again regular.

5. Let us write down our system

$$\begin{array}{l} a_{11}x_1+\dots+a_{1n}x_n=k_1 \\ \dots\dots\quad\dots \\ a_{n1}x_n+\dots+a_{nn}x_n=k_n, \end{array} \tag{6}$$

and suppose the equations numbered so that $a_{11} \neq 0$ (by operation α). This is possible provided that the first column contains a non-zero element. Now that is always the case, for if not, then the first column would be the zero-column and the columns of our system could not be linearly independent. We can reduce the coefficient of x_1 in the first equation to 1 by multiplying that equation by $1/a_{11}$ (operation β). If we now subtract a_{i1} times the first equation from the i-th equation, for $i=2, \dots, n$ (operation γ), we obtain a system in which x_1 occurs with the coefficient 1 in the first equation and with the coefficient 0 in the remaining ones. Thus the new system has the form

$$\begin{array}{r} x_1+b_{12}x_2+\dots+b_{1n}x_n=l_1 \\ b_{22}x_2+\dots+b_{2n}x_n=l_2 \\ \dots\dots\quad\dots \\ b_{n2}x_2+\dots+b_{nn}x_n=l_n, \end{array} \tag{7}$$

where

$$b_{ij}=a_{ij}-\frac{a_{i1}}{a_{11}}a_{1j}, \qquad l_i=k_i-\frac{a_{i1}}{a_{11}}k_1 \qquad (i,j=2,\ldots,n).$$

The effect of the operations has been to eliminate x_1 from all equations but the first. Since we have used only α, β, γ, this system is equivalent to the original system, and it is again regular, by the result of No. 4.

6. We continue the solution by applying the same process to the last $n-1$ equations of (7), which constitute an $(n-1)\times(n-1)$ system, but in order to be able to do so we must show that this system of $n-1$ equations is regular.

We have to show that when we replace l_i by 0 in (7), the last $n-1$ equations have only the trivial solution. Suppose this is not so, and let $(u_2, \ldots, u_n)$ be a non-trivial solution of these $n-1$ equations. Then we obtain a solution $(u_1, u_2, \ldots, u_n)$ of the whole n equations by taking $u_1=-b_{12}u_2- \ldots -b_{1n}u_n$. For this satisfies the first equation, and the others are satisfied by hypothesis. Further, the solution is non-trivial because at least one of $u_2, \ldots, u_n$ is $\neq 0$, again by hypothesis. This shows that the n columns of (7) are linearly dependent, in contradiction to the fact that this system is regular. Therefore the last $n-1$ equations in (7) do constitute a regular system.

7. We have now reduced the proof of Theorem 1, for a system of n equations, to the proof of Theorem 1, for a system of $n-1$ equations, and we can complete the proof by using mathematical induction. This may be used whenever we want to prove a proposition P_n for all integers n. We first prove P_1 and then, for any $n\geqslant 2$, show that P_n follows from P_{n-1}. The principle of induction then states that P_n is true for all n.

To apply this remark to our case we first have to prove Theorem 1 for systems of order 1, that is, single equations in one unknown. The equation $ax=k$ is regular provided that $a \neq 0$, and then the equation has the unique solution $x=k/a$. Now we use the induction hypothesis on (7): the last $n-1$

equations have the unique solution

$$\begin{aligned} x_2 &= r_2 \\ &\cdot \\ &\cdot \\ &\cdot \\ x_n &= r_n, \end{aligned}$$

so that we obtain a system equivalent to (7) as follows:

$$\begin{array}{l} x_1+b_{12}x_2+\ldots+b_{1n}x_n=l_1 \\ \qquad x_2 \qquad\qquad\qquad =r_2 \\ \qquad\qquad x_3 \qquad\qquad =r_3 \\ \qquad\qquad\qquad \ldots \\ \qquad\qquad\qquad\qquad x_n=r_n. \end{array}$$

If we subtract b_{1j} times the j-th equation from the first equation, for $j=2, \ldots, n$, we obtain an equivalent system

$$\begin{aligned} x_1 &= r_1 \\ x_2 &= r_2 \\ &\ldots \\ x_n &= r_n, \end{aligned}$$

where $r_1=l_1-\sum_{j=2}^{n} b_{1j}r_j$. Hence the original system (6) has the unique solution $\mathbf{x}=(r_1, \ldots, r_n)'$, and this completes the proof of the theorem.

8. To illustrate Theorem 1 let us take the system

$$\begin{aligned} x_1+5x_2+2x_3&=9 \\ x_1+x_2+7x_3&=6 \\ -3x_2+4x_3&=-2, \end{aligned} \tag{8}$$

and apply the method described in Nos. 5–7. For brevity we shall not write down the equations in full each time, but merely give the scheme of coefficients. The given system may be written

$$\begin{array}{rrr|r} 1 & 5 & 2 & 9 \\ 1 & 1 & 7 & 6 \\ 0 & -3 & 4 & -2, \end{array}$$

where the position of the equality sign is indicated by a vertical line. The coefficient of x_1 in the first equation is already 1; as the next step we replace row_2 of the scheme by $\text{row}_2 - \text{row}_1$ and obtain

$$\begin{array}{rrr|r} 1 & 5 & 2 & 9 \\ 0 & -4 & 5 & -3 \\ 0 & -3 & 4 & -2. \end{array}$$

Next we divide row_2 by -4 and then replace row_3 by $\text{row}_3 + 3\text{row}_2$:

$$\begin{array}{rrr|r} 1 & 5 & 2 & 9 \\ 0 & 1 & -\frac{5}{4} & \frac{3}{4} \\ 0 & 0 & \frac{1}{4} & \frac{1}{4}. \end{array}$$

We may as well complete the elimination of x_2 at this stage by subtracting 5row_2 from row_1:

$$\begin{array}{rrr|r} 1 & 0 & \frac{33}{4} & \frac{21}{4} \\ 0 & 1 & -\frac{5}{4} & \frac{3}{4} \\ 0 & 0 & \frac{1}{4} & \frac{1}{4}. \end{array}$$

Finally we multiply row_3 by 4 and subtract appropriate multiples from row_1 and row_2:

$$\begin{array}{rrr|r} 1 & 0 & 0 & -3 \\ 0 & 1 & 0 & 2 \\ 0 & 0 & 1 & 1. \end{array}$$

We now obtain the solution by writing the rows of this scheme as equations:

$$x_1 = -3$$
$$x_2 = 2$$
$$x_3 = 1.$$

In order to check this solution we need only substitute the values found for x_1, x_2, x_3 in (8).

It is not necessary to follow this procedure exactly, as long as we use only the operations α, β, γ. By putting in extra steps we can sometimes make the calculations easier, e.g. in the above example we could avoid the occurrence of fractions by proceeding as follows (after the reduction of the first column):

$$\begin{array}{rrr|r} 1 & 5 & 2 & 9 \\ 0 & -4 & 5 & -3 \\ 0 & -3 & 4 & -2 \end{array} \quad R_2 \rightarrow R_2 - R_3 \quad \begin{array}{rrr|r} 1 & 5 & 2 & 9 \\ 0 & -1 & 1 & -1 \\ 0 & -3 & 4 & -2 \end{array} \quad R_2 \rightarrow -R_2$$

$$\begin{array}{rrr|r} 1 & 5 & 2 & 9 \\ 0 & 1 & -1 & 1 \\ 0 & -3 & 4 & -2 \end{array} \quad R_3 \rightarrow R_3 + 3R_2 \quad \begin{array}{rrr|r} 1 & 0 & 7 & 4 \\ 0 & 1 & -1 & 1 \\ 0 & 0 & 1 & 1 \end{array} \quad \begin{array}{l} R_1 \rightarrow R_1 - 7R_3 \\ R_2 \rightarrow R_2 + R_3 \end{array}$$

$$\begin{array}{rrr|r} 1 & 0 & 0 & -3 \\ 0 & 1 & 0 & 2 \\ 0 & 0 & 1 & 1. \end{array}$$

The operations performed are indicated before each scheme, thus $R_2 \rightarrow R_2 - R_3$ before the second scheme means that this scheme is obtained from the first by replacing row_2 by $\text{row}_2 - \text{row}_3$. Similarly $R_1 \leftrightarrow R_2$ before a scheme would mean that it has been obtained from the previous scheme by interchanging row_1 and row_2.

Sometimes it is quicker to stop[1] when we have reached the 'triangular' form[2] (cf. the second scheme on p. 20).

$$\begin{array}{rrr|r} 1 & 5 & 2 & 9 \\ 0 & 1 & -\frac{5}{4} & \frac{3}{4} \\ 0 & 0 & \frac{1}{4} & \frac{1}{4} \end{array}$$

and solve the corresponding equations

$$\begin{aligned} x_1 + 5x_2 + 2x_3 &= 9 \\ x_2 - \tfrac{5}{4}x_3 &= \tfrac{3}{4} \\ \tfrac{1}{4}x_3 &= \tfrac{1}{4} \end{aligned}$$

recursively, beginning with the last equation and substituting into the previous equations in turn: $x_3 = 1$, $x_2 = \frac{3}{4} + \frac{5}{4}x_3 = 2$, $x_1 = 9 - 5x_2 - 2x_3 = -3$.

[1] This is particularly so when a system is solved by machine.

[2] So called because on the left all the coefficients outside a certain triangle are zero.

9. As a second illustration we consider the equations

$$\begin{aligned} x_1-2x_2-\ 7x_3+\ 7x_4&=\ \ 5\\ -x_1+2x_2+\ 8x_3-\ 5x_4&=-7\\ 3x_1-4x_2-17x_3+13x_4&=\ 14\\ 2x_1-2x_2-11x_3+\ 8x_4&=\ \ 7. \end{aligned}$$

We shall write down the scheme with the successive reductions:

$$\begin{array}{rrrr|r} 1 & -2 & -7 & 7 & 5\\ -1 & 2 & 8 & -5 & -7\\ 3 & -4 & -17 & 13 & 14\\ 2 & -2 & -11 & 8 & 7 \end{array} \quad \begin{array}{l} R_2\to R_2+R_1\\ R_3\to R_3-3R_1\\ R_4\to R_4-2R_1 \end{array} \quad \begin{array}{rrrr|r} 1 & -2 & -7 & 7 & 5\\ 0 & 0 & 1 & 2 & -2\\ 0 & 2 & 4 & -8 & -1\\ 0 & 2 & 3 & -6 & -3 \end{array}$$

$$R_2\leftrightarrow R_3 \quad \begin{array}{rrrr|r} 1 & -2 & -7 & 7 & 5\\ 0 & 2 & 4 & -8 & -1\\ 0 & 0 & 1 & 2 & -2\\ 0 & 2 & 3 & -6 & -3 \end{array} \quad R_2\to \tfrac{1}{2}R_2 \quad \begin{array}{rrrr|r} 1 & -2 & -7 & 7 & 5\\ 0 & 1 & 2 & -4 & -\frac{1}{2}\\ 0 & 0 & 1 & 2 & -2\\ 0 & 2 & 3 & -6 & -3 \end{array}$$

$$\begin{array}{l} R_1\to R_1+2R_2\\ R_4\to R_4-2R_2 \end{array} \quad \begin{array}{rrrr|r} 1 & 0 & -3 & -1 & 4\\ 0 & 1 & 2 & -4 & -\frac{1}{2}\\ 0 & 0 & 1 & 2 & -2\\ 0 & 0 & -1 & 2 & -2 \end{array} \quad \begin{array}{l} R_1\to R_1+3R_3\\ R_2\to R_2-2R_3\\ R_4\to R_4+R_3 \end{array}$$

$$\begin{array}{rrrr|r} 1 & 0 & 0 & 5 & -2\\ 0 & 1 & 0 & -8 & 3\frac{1}{2}\\ 0 & 0 & 1 & 2 & -2\\ 0 & 0 & 0 & 4 & -4 \end{array} \quad \begin{array}{l} R_4\to \tfrac{1}{4}R_4\\ R_1\to R_1-5R_4\\ R_2\to R_2+8R_4\\ R_3\to R_3-2R_4 \end{array} \quad \begin{array}{rrrr|r} 1 & 0 & 0 & 0 & 3\\ 0 & 1 & 0 & 0 & -4\frac{1}{2}\\ 0 & 0 & 1 & 0 & 0\\ 0 & 0 & 0 & 1 & -1 \end{array}$$

The solution is $x_1=3$, $x_2=-4\frac{1}{2}$, $x_3=0$, $x_4=-1$. Here we have had to renumber the equations before we could reduce the second column. Evidently we cannot avoid fractions in the process this time, since they appear in the solution.

If we solve the system via the triangular form, the successive schemes are

$$\begin{array}{rrrr|r} 1 & -2 & -7 & 7 & 5 \\ -1 & 2 & 8 & -5 & -7 \\ 3 & -4 & -17 & 13 & 14 \\ 2 & -2 & -11 & 8 & 7 \end{array} \quad \begin{array}{l} R_2 \to R_2+R_1 \\ R_3 \to R_3-3R_1 \\ R_4 \to R_4-2R_1 \end{array} \quad \begin{array}{rrrr|r} 1 & -2 & -7 & 7 & 5 \\ 0 & 0 & 1 & 2 & -2 \\ 0 & 2 & 4 & -8 & -1 \\ 0 & 2 & 3 & -6 & -3 \end{array}$$

$$R_2 \longleftrightarrow R_3 \quad \begin{array}{rrrr|r} 1 & -2 & -7 & 7 & 5 \\ 0 & 2 & 4 & -8 & -1 \\ 0 & 0 & 1 & 2 & -2 \\ 0 & 2 & 3 & -6 & -3 \end{array} \quad R_2 \to \tfrac{1}{2}R_2$$

$$\begin{array}{rrrr|r} 1 & -2 & -7 & 7 & 5 \\ 0 & 1 & 2 & -4 & -\frac{1}{2} \\ 0 & 0 & 1 & 2 & -2 \\ 0 & 2 & 3 & -6 & -3 \end{array} \quad R_4 \to R_4-2R_2 \quad \begin{array}{rrrr|r} 1 & -2 & -7 & 7 & 5 \\ 0 & 1 & 2 & -4 & -\frac{1}{2} \\ 0 & 0 & 1 & 2 & -2 \\ 0 & 0 & -1 & 2 & -2 \end{array}$$

$$R_4 \to R_4+R_3 \quad \begin{array}{rrrr|r} 1 & -2 & -7 & 7 & 5 \\ 0 & 1 & 2 & -4 & -\frac{1}{2} \\ 0 & 0 & 1 & 2 & -2 \\ 0 & 0 & 0 & 4 & -4, \end{array}$$

whence $x_4=-1$, $x_3=-2-2x_4=0$, $x_2=-\frac{1}{2}+4x_4-2x_3=-4\frac{1}{2}$, $x_1=5-7x_4+7x_3+2x_2=3$.

10. An $n \times n$ system in which all the coefficients $a_{n1}, a_{n2}, \ldots, a_{nn}$ of the last equation are zero, cannot be regular. For if all the coefficients on the left of the last equation vanish, then, for the system to have a solution, the term on the right of the last equation must vanish too, i.e. $k_n=0$. Thus the system has no solution if $k_n \neq 0$, whereas a regular system has a solution whatever the vector $\mathbf{k}$ on the right (cf. Theorem 1′, II.2); hence the system is not regular. The result may also be stated as follows, if we remember that a regular system is just one whose n columns are linearly independent:

If n vectors of dimension n have their last component equal to zero, they are linearly dependent.

From this proposition we can easily deduce the important

Theorem 2. *Any $n+1$ vectors of dimension n are linearly dependent.*

For if $\mathbf{u}_i=(u_{i1}, \ldots, u_{in})$ $(i=1, \ldots, n+1)$ are the given vectors of dimension n, we consider the $n+1$ vectors $\mathbf{u}_i^* = (u_{i1}, \ldots, u_{in}, 0)$ of dimension $n+1$. These vectors have 0 as their last component and therefore, by the result just proved, are linearly dependent, say

$$\mathbf{u}_{n+1}^*=\lambda_1\mathbf{u}_1^*+ \ldots +\lambda_n\mathbf{u}_n^*.$$

Equating components in this relation, we find

$$u_{n+1j}=\lambda_1 u_{1j}+ \ldots +\lambda_n u_{nj} \qquad (j=1, \ldots, n),$$

whence

$$\mathbf{u}_{n+1}=\lambda_1\mathbf{u}_1+ \ldots +\lambda_n\mathbf{u}_n,$$

i.e. the given vectors are linearly dependent, as we wished to show.

11. As an application of Theorem 2 we note that in n dimensions any n vectors which are linearly independent form a basis for the space of all n-vectors. For let $\mathbf{v}_1, \ldots, \mathbf{v}_n$ be any set of n linearly independent vectors in the space of all n-vectors, and consider any vector $\mathbf{x}$ in this space. The $n+1$ vectors $\mathbf{x}, \mathbf{v}_1, \ldots, \mathbf{v}_n$ are linearly dependent, by Theorem 2: thus we have a relation

$$\alpha\mathbf{x}+\alpha_1\mathbf{v}_1+ \ldots +\alpha_n\mathbf{v}_n=\mathbf{0}, \tag{9}$$

where not all of $\alpha, \alpha_1, \ldots, \alpha_n$ are zero. If α were zero, then (9) would be a non-trivial relation between $\mathbf{v}_1, \ldots, \mathbf{v}_n$, which contradicts the fact that these vectors are independent. So α must be $\neq 0$, and writing $\xi_i=-\alpha_i/\alpha$, we have

$$\mathbf{x}=\xi_1\mathbf{v}_1+ \ldots +\xi_n\mathbf{v}_n,$$

which expresses $\mathbf{x}$ as a linear combination of $\mathbf{v}_1, \ldots, \mathbf{v}_n$. Thus the $\mathbf{v}_i$ span the space of n-vectors, and they therefore form a basis for it.

We can now also prove that any two bases of a given space have the same number of elements. For let $\mathbf{u}_1, \ldots, \mathbf{u}_m$, $\mathbf{v}_1, \ldots, \mathbf{v}_n$ be two bases of a vector space V. Every vector $\mathbf{x}$ of V can be uniquely expressed as a linear combination of the basis-vectors $\mathbf{v}_1, \ldots, \mathbf{v}_n$,

$$\mathbf{x}=\xi_1\mathbf{v}_1+ \ldots +\xi_n\mathbf{v}_n,$$

and we may take $\xi_1, \ldots, \xi_n$ to be the components of $\mathbf{x}$ (see I.9). In terms of these components the vectors of V are n-dimensional, and therefore any $n+1$ vectors of V are linearly dependent. In particular, if $m>n$, then $\mathbf{u}_1, \ldots, \mathbf{u}_{n+1}$ would be dependent, which is impossible, because these vectors are in the set $\mathbf{u}_1, \ldots, \mathbf{u}_m$ which is independent. Therefore $m \leqslant n$; by interchanging the roles of the bases $\mathbf{u}_1, \ldots, \mathbf{u}_m$ and $\mathbf{v}_1, \ldots, \mathbf{v}_n$ we see that $n \leqslant m$, and so $m=n$, as we wished to show.

This shows that the dimension of any space (such as the space of all n-vectors) is uniquely determined and may be found by counting the number of elements in any basis of the space.

EXERCISES ON CHAPTER II

1. The following schemes represent regular systems of equations, in the notation of II.8. Find the solution in each case.

$$\text{(i)}\ \begin{array}{ccc|c} 2 & 4 & 1 & 5 \\ 1 & 1 & 1 & 6 \\ 2 & 3 & 1 & 6 \end{array} \qquad \text{(ii)}\ \begin{array}{ccc|c} 5 & 15 & -10 & 0 \\ -2 & -2 & -4 & 4 \\ 3 & 4 & 1 & -5 \end{array} \qquad \text{(iii)}\ \begin{array}{ccc|c} 1 & 4 & 11 & 7 \\ 2 & 8 & 16 & 8 \\ 1 & 6 & 17 & 9 \end{array}$$

$$\text{(iv)}\ \begin{array}{ccc|c} 3 & -3 & 5 & 6 \\ 1 & 7 & 5 & 4 \\ 5 & 10 & 15 & 9 \end{array} \qquad \text{(v)}\ \begin{array}{ccc|c} 3 & 2 & -1 & 0 \\ 1 & 7 & 5 & 0 \\ -1 & 0 & 1 & 0 \end{array} \qquad \text{(vi)}\ \begin{array}{cccc|c} 2 & 1 & 2 & -1 & 0 \\ 6 & 8 & 12 & -13 & -21 \\ 10 & 2 & 2 & 3 & 21 \\ -4 & 0 & 1 & -3 & -13 \end{array}$$

$$\text{(vii)}\ \begin{array}{cccc|c} 2 & -1 & 4 & 7 & 10 \\ 0 & 1 & 0 & -5 & -6 \\ 0 & 0 & -3 & 2 & 8 \\ 0 & 0 & 0 & 1 & 1 \end{array} \qquad \text{(viii)}\ \begin{array}{cccc|c} 4 & -8 & 4 & -20 & 0 \\ 3 & -6 & 4 & -14 & 4 \\ -2 & 4 & -4 & 9 & 5 \\ 4 & -7 & 5 & -8 & 6. \end{array}$$

2. Show that the triangular system

$$\begin{array}{ccccc|c} a_{11} & a_{12} & a_{13} & \ldots & a_{1n} & k_1 \\ 0 & a_{22} & a_{23} & \ldots & a_{2n} & k_2 \\ . & . & . & \ldots & . & . \\ 0 & 0 & 0 & \ldots & a_{nn} & k_n, \end{array}$$

is regular if and only if all the diagonal coefficients $a_{11}, \ldots, a_{nn}$ are different from zero.

3. Show that any collection of n-vectors which is closed under addition and multiplication by scalars (i.e. which contains with $\mathbf{u}$, $\mathbf{v}$ the vectors $\mathbf{u}+\mathbf{v}$ and $\lambda\mathbf{u}$ for any scalar λ) forms a vector space and that its dimension is at most n. Such a space is called a *subspace* of the space of all n-vectors. (Use I.9 and II.11 to find a basis, by choosing as many linearly independent vectors from the collection as possible.)

CHAPTER THREE

Matrices

1. There is still another way of regarding an $m \times n$ system of equations, which will lead to an even shorter way of writing it than in ch. II. Let us first write the system as

$$\begin{array}{c} a_{11}x_1 + \dots + a_{1n}x_n = y_1 \\ \cdot \quad \cdot \quad \cdots \quad \cdots \\ a_{m1}x_1 + \dots + a_{mn}x_n = y_m, \end{array} \tag{1}$$

where we have replaced the constants k_i on the right by variables y_i. If we take $\mathbf{x} = (x_1, \dots, x_n)'$ and $\mathbf{y} = (y_1, \dots, y_m)'$ to be column-vectors, we may regard the set of coefficients (a_{ij}) in (1) as an operator which acts on $\mathbf{x}$ to produce $\mathbf{y}$. In this sense we write (1) as

$$\begin{pmatrix} a_{11} & a_{12} & \dots & a_{1n} \\ a_{21} & a_{22} & \dots & a_{2n} \\ \cdot & \cdot & \cdots & \cdot \\ a_{m1} & a_{m2} & \dots & a_{mn} \end{pmatrix} \begin{pmatrix} x_1 \\ x_2 \\ \cdot \\ x_n \end{pmatrix} = \begin{pmatrix} y_1 \\ y_2 \\ \cdot \\ y_m \end{pmatrix}. \tag{2}$$

The rectangular array of coefficients

$$\begin{pmatrix} a_{11} & a_{12} & \dots & a_{1n} \\ a_{21} & a_{22} & \dots & a_{2n} \\ \cdot & \cdot & \cdots & \cdot \\ a_{m1} & a_{m2} & \dots & a_{mn} \end{pmatrix} \tag{3}$$

is called a *matrix* with the *elements* a_{ij}, and the left-hand side of (2) may be regarded as the 'product' of this matrix by the vector $\mathbf{x}$. A comparison with (1) shows that this product is evaluated by multiplying the elements of the j-th column of (3) by x_j and adding the column-vectors so obtained. The sum of these vectors has its i-th component equal to $a_{i1}x_1 + \dots + a_{in}x_n$ $(i = 1, \dots, m)$, and the vector equation (2) states that this vector is equal to the column-vector $\mathbf{y}=(y_1, \ldots, y_m)'$, which is in fact a restatement of the equations (1).

If we denote the matrix (3) by **A**, we may write (2) more briefly as

$$\mathbf{Ax}=\mathbf{y}.$$

The matrix (3) has m rows and n columns which correspond to the rows and columns of the equations (1), and it is briefly described as an $m \times n$ matrix; if $m=n$ we say that **A** is a square matrix of *order n*. In (2) we applied the matrix **A** to **x** and obtained the result **y**. From the meaning given to equation (2) it follows that an $m \times n$ matrix can only be applied to an n-vector, and the result is necessarily an m-vector.

2. The introduction of matrices enables us to write many formulae more compactly and in a more suggestive way, just as vectors already helped us in ch. II to obtain a clearer picture of the solutions of linear equations. We shall therefore in this chapter introduce the basic rules of calculating with matrices.

Since the coefficients in (1) are arbitrary, it follows that any mn numbers a_{ij}, arranged in a rectangle as in (3), form a matrix. Matrices will usually be denoted by capitals in heavy type: **A**, **B**, . . . ; more explicitly we may write the matrix (3) as (a_{ij}), where the first suffix (in this case i) indicates the row and the second suffix (here j) indicates the column. Of course if the elements of the matrix have definite numerical values, the matrix must be written out in full. Thus, e.g., the matrix of the first example considered in the Introduction is

$$\begin{pmatrix} 3 & 2 \\ 2 & 5 \end{pmatrix}.$$

3. A most important property of matrices is expressed in the equations

$$\mathbf{A}(\mathbf{u}+\mathbf{v})=\mathbf{Au}+\mathbf{Av}, \quad \mathbf{A}(\lambda\mathbf{u})=\lambda\mathbf{Au}, \tag{4}$$

where **A** is an $m \times n$ matrix, **u** and **v** are n-vectors and λ is a scalar.[1] Their verification is easy and is left to the reader.

[1] The properties expressed in (4) are often summed up by saying that the expression **Au** is *linear* in **u**, or that **A** is a *linear* operator.

E.g. for $m=n=2$, the second equation states

$$\begin{pmatrix} a_{11}\lambda u_1+a_{12}\lambda u_2 \\ a_{21}\lambda u_1+a_{22}\lambda u_2 \end{pmatrix}=\begin{pmatrix} \lambda(a_{11}u_1+a_{12}u_2) \\ \lambda(a_{21}u_1+a_{22}u_2) \end{pmatrix}.$$

The equations (4) may be used to express $\mathbf{Ax}$ as a linear combination of the vectors $\mathbf{Ae}_i$, where the $\mathbf{e}_i$ are the n basis-vectors[1] introduced in I.8. For if $\mathbf{x}=(x_1, \ldots, x_n)'$, then $\mathbf{x}=x_1\mathbf{e}_1+\ldots+x_n\mathbf{e}_n$, and hence

$$\begin{aligned}\mathbf{Ax}=\mathbf{A}(x_1\mathbf{e}_1+\ldots+x_n\mathbf{e}_n)&=\mathbf{A}(x_1\mathbf{e}_1)+\ldots+\mathbf{A}(x_n\mathbf{e}_n)\\ &=x_1\mathbf{Ae}_1+\ldots+x_n\mathbf{Ae}_n,\end{aligned}$$

by repeated use of (4). Thus we have expressed $\mathbf{Ax}$ as a linear combination of the n vectors $\mathbf{Ae}_1, \ldots, \mathbf{Ae}_n$, which of course do not depend on the choice of $\mathbf{x}$. These vectors $\mathbf{Ae}_j$ are nothing but the columns of $\mathbf{A}$, thus $\mathbf{Ae}_1=(a_{11}, a_{21}, \ldots, a_{m1})'$, $\mathbf{Ae}_2=(a_{12}, a_{22}, \ldots, a_{m2})'$, etc.

4. Two matrices $\mathbf{A}=(a_{ij})$ and $\mathbf{B}=(b_{ij})$ are said to be equal: $\mathbf{A}=\mathbf{B}$, if they have the same number of rows and columns—say they are both $m\times n$ matrices—and if corresponding elements are equal:

$$a_{ij}=b_{ij} \qquad (i=1, \ldots, m;\, j=1, \ldots, n).$$

Thus a matrix equation between $m\times n$ matrices is equivalent to mn scalar equations. In fact we may look on $m\times n$ matrices as vectors in mn dimensions, whose components are arranged not as a row or column but as a rectangle.

It follows from the definition that if $\mathbf{A}=\mathbf{B}$, then $\mathbf{Au}=\mathbf{Bu}$ for any vector $\mathbf{u}$ (of dimension equal to the number of columns of $\mathbf{A}$ or $\mathbf{B}$). Conversely, if $\mathbf{A}$ and $\mathbf{B}$ are $m\times n$ matrices such that $\mathbf{Au}=\mathbf{Bu}$ for any n-vector $\mathbf{u}$, then $\mathbf{A}=\mathbf{B}$. For if we take the basis-vector $\mathbf{e}_j$ for $\mathbf{u}$ we see that the j-th column of $\mathbf{A}$ must be the same as the j-th column of $\mathbf{B}$, i.e. $a_{ij}=b_{ij}$ $(i=1, \ldots, m)$. Since this holds for $j=1, \ldots, n$, it follows that corresponding elements of $\mathbf{A}$ and $\mathbf{B}$ are equal, whence $\mathbf{A}=\mathbf{B}$. Thus we have shown that

two $m\times n$ matrices $\mathbf{A}$, $\mathbf{B}$ *are equal if and only if*

$$\mathbf{Ae}_j=\mathbf{Be}_j \qquad (j=1, \ldots, n),$$

where $\mathbf{e}_1, \ldots, \mathbf{e}_n$ *are the basis-vectors defined in* I.8.

[1] We now regard the $\mathbf{e}_i$ as column-vectors.

5. The addition of matrices, and the multiplication by a scalar, are defined as follows. If $\mathbf{A}=(a_{ij})$, $\mathbf{B}=(b_{ij})$ are two $m\times n$ matrices and λ is a scalar, we put

$$\mathbf{A}+\mathbf{B}=(a_{ij}+b_{ij})\quad \lambda\mathbf{A}=(\lambda a_{ij}).$$

Thus we add (and multiply by scalars) 'component-wise', just as we do for vectors, and the same rules hold for the addition of matrices, as for vectors (cf. I.3-4). Examples:

$$2\begin{pmatrix}3 & -2 & 8\\ 1 & 0 & 5\end{pmatrix}=\begin{pmatrix}6 & -4 & 16\\ 2 & 0 & 10\end{pmatrix},$$

$$\begin{pmatrix}4 & 7 & -1\\ 3 & -2 & 5\end{pmatrix}+\begin{pmatrix}3 & -5 & 6\\ -8 & 1 & 9\end{pmatrix}=\begin{pmatrix}7 & 2 & 5\\ -5 & -1 & 14\end{pmatrix}.$$

The $m\times n$ matrix whose elements are all zero is called the *zero-matrix* (of m rows and n columns) and is denoted by **O**, the number of rows and columns being usually understood from the context.

The operations just defined satisfy the important rules

$$(\mathbf{A}+\mathbf{B})\mathbf{u}=\mathbf{A}\mathbf{u}+\mathbf{B}\mathbf{u},\quad (\lambda\mathbf{A})\mathbf{u}=\lambda(\mathbf{A}\mathbf{u}). \tag{5}$$

The proof is quite straightforward: it is only necessary to show that the two sides agree when $\mathbf{u}=\mathbf{e}_j$ $(j=1,\ldots,n)$, and this may be left to the reader. We content ourselves with an illustration: If $\mathbf{A}=\begin{pmatrix}3 & 1\\ -2 & 5\end{pmatrix}$ and $\mathbf{B}=\begin{pmatrix}2 & 4\\ 6 & -3\end{pmatrix}$, then $2\mathbf{A}-3\mathbf{B}$ $=\begin{pmatrix}0 & -10\\ -22 & 19\end{pmatrix}$; further, if $\mathbf{u}=(1, 1)'$, then

$$2(\mathbf{A}\mathbf{u})-3(\mathbf{B}\mathbf{u})=2\begin{pmatrix}3 & 1\\ -2 & 5\end{pmatrix}\begin{pmatrix}1\\ 1\end{pmatrix}-3\begin{pmatrix}2 & 4\\ 6 & -3\end{pmatrix}\begin{pmatrix}1\\ 1\end{pmatrix}=2\begin{pmatrix}4\\ 3\end{pmatrix}-3\begin{pmatrix}6\\ 3\end{pmatrix}$$

$$=\begin{pmatrix}-10\\ -3\end{pmatrix},\quad (2\mathbf{A}-3\mathbf{B})\mathbf{u}=\begin{pmatrix}0 & -10\\ -22 & 19\end{pmatrix}\begin{pmatrix}1\\ 1\end{pmatrix}=\begin{pmatrix}-10\\ -3\end{pmatrix}.$$

6. A further operation is the multiplication of matrices. In order to describe this we shall first take the case of square matrices. If $\mathbf{A}=(a_{ij})$ and $\mathbf{B}=(b_{ij})$ are square matrices of order n, then the product of **A** by **B**, denoted by **AB**, is defined to be the $n\times n$ matrix $\mathbf{C}=(c_{ik})$ with elements

$$c_{ik}=\sum_j a_{ij}b_{jk}. \tag{6}$$

As an illustration we write out **AB** in the case $n=2$:

$$\mathbf{AB}=\begin{pmatrix} a_{11}b_{11}+a_{12}b_{21} & a_{11}b_{12}+a_{12}b_{22} \\ a_{21}b_{11}+a_{22}b_{21} & a_{21}b_{12}+a_{22}b_{22} \end{pmatrix}.$$

In the general case the definition (6) of $\mathbf{C}(=\mathbf{AB})$ may be described as follows: c_{11}, the '(1,1)-element' of **AB**, is obtained by multiplying the elements of the first *row* of **A** by the corresponding elements of the first *column* of **B** and adding the results. The (1,2)-element, c_{12}, is obtained by multiplying the elements of the first row of **A** by the corresponding elements from the second column of **B** and adding, and so on; generally, to obtain the (i,k)-element c_{ik} of **AB** we use the i-th row of **A** and the k-th column of **B**. To give a numerical example, let

$$\mathbf{A}=\begin{pmatrix} 3 & 1 \\ -2 & 5 \end{pmatrix},\ \mathbf{B}=\begin{pmatrix} 2 & 4 \\ 6 & -3 \end{pmatrix},\ \text{then } \mathbf{AB}=\begin{pmatrix} 12 & 9 \\ 26 & -23 \end{pmatrix}.$$

In order to understand the idea behind this definition, let us take an n-vector **u** and form **Bu**. This is again an n-vector, and so we can apply **A**; the result is the vector $\mathbf{v}=\mathbf{A}(\mathbf{Bu})$, with the components

$$v_i=\sum_j a_{ij}\Big(\sum_k b_{jk}u_k\Big), \tag{7}$$

for $\Sigma b_{jk}u_k$ is just the j-th component of the vector **Bu**. On the right-hand side of (7) we have a sum of n expressions each of which is itself a sum of n terms, thus altogether we have n^2 terms to add; now it does not matter in which order we add them, and so we may first add all the terms in which $k=1$, then the terms with $k=2$, and so on. In this way we obtain, for the sum on the right of (7), $\sum_j a_{ij}b_{j1}u_1+\sum_j a_{ij}b_{j2}u_2+\ldots+\sum_j a_{ij}b_{jn}u_n$, or more briefly, $\sum_k\Big(\sum_j a_{ij}b_{jk}\Big)u_k$. Thus we can write (7) as

$$v_i=\sum_k c_{ik}u_k, \tag{8}$$

where the c_{ik} are the elements of the product **AB**. In vector notation equation (8) reads

$$\mathbf{A}(\mathbf{B}\mathbf{u})=(\mathbf{A}\mathbf{B})\mathbf{u}, \tag{9}$$

and it was with this equation in mind that the definition of the product was chosen.

Again there are a number of laws satisfied by matrix multiplication:

M.1. $(\mathbf{AB})\mathbf{C}=\mathbf{A}(\mathbf{BC})$, (associative law)

M.2. $\mathbf{A}(\mathbf{B}+\mathbf{D})=\mathbf{AB}+\mathbf{AD}$ } (distributive laws).

M.3. $(\mathbf{B}+\mathbf{D})\mathbf{C}=\mathbf{BC}+\mathbf{DC}$ }

These rules are proved by showing that the two sides of the equation, when applied to an arbitrary vector **u**, give the same result (cf. No. 4). For example, M.1 follows because

$$[(\mathbf{AB})\mathbf{C}]\mathbf{u}=(\mathbf{AB})(\mathbf{Cu})=\mathbf{A}[\mathbf{B}(\mathbf{Cu})]=\mathbf{A}[(\mathbf{BC})\mathbf{u}]=[\mathbf{A}(\mathbf{BC})]\mathbf{u},$$

where we have used (9) at each step. M.2 and M.3 may be proved similarly, using (4) and (5) respectively. Of course all these rules may also be verified by direct calculation, using the definition (6) of the product **AB**.

It is important to note that the order of the factors in a matrix-product is material, for we have

$$\mathbf{AB}\neq\mathbf{BA},$$

except in special cases. Consider, e.g., the matrices used in the last numerical example. If we compute **BA**, we find

$$\begin{pmatrix} 2 & 4 \\ 6 & -3 \end{pmatrix}\begin{pmatrix} 3 & 1 \\ -2 & 5 \end{pmatrix}=\begin{pmatrix} -2 & 22 \\ 24 & -9 \end{pmatrix},$$

which is different from **AB**. An even simpler example is the following:

$$\mathbf{A}=\begin{pmatrix} 1 & 0 \\ 0 & 0 \end{pmatrix},\ \mathbf{B}=\begin{pmatrix} 0 & 1 \\ 0 & 0 \end{pmatrix},\ \mathbf{AB}=\begin{pmatrix} 0 & 1 \\ 0 & 0 \end{pmatrix},\ \mathbf{BA}=\begin{pmatrix} 0 & 0 \\ 0 & 0 \end{pmatrix}.$$

7. The behaviour of the zero-matrix resembles that of the scalar zero under multiplication as well as addition. Thus $\mathbf{AO}=\mathbf{OA}=\mathbf{O}$ for any $n\times n$ matrix **A** (where **O** is the $n\times n$ zero-matrix). However, the product of two matrices may be **O**

even when neither factor is **O** (see the example at the end of No. 6).

There is also an analogue of the number 1. This is the square matrix

$$\begin{pmatrix} 1 & 0 & 0 \dots 0 \\ 0 & 1 & 0 \dots 0 \\ 0 & 0 & 1 \dots 0 \\ . & . & \dots . \\ 0 & 0 & 0 \dots 1 \end{pmatrix}$$

whose i-th column has 1 in the i-th place and 0 elsewhere. This matrix is denoted by **I** and is called the *unit-matrix*. Since its columns are just the vectors $\mathbf{e}_j$ we have $\mathbf{I}\mathbf{e}_j = \mathbf{e}_j$ $(j = 1, \dots, n)$. More generally we have

$$\mathbf{I}\mathbf{u} = \mathbf{u} \qquad (10)$$

for every vector **u**, as follows by writing down the system of equations corresponding to the left-hand side of (10). We also note that for any $n \times n$ matrix **A**.

$$\mathbf{IA} = \mathbf{AI} = \mathbf{A}.$$

The verification of these equations is a simple application of the multiplication rule (6), and may be left to the reader.

8. In the definition of the product **AB** given above we have supposed that **A** and **B** are square matrices of the same order n. But this is not necessary; the definition can be used for any matrices **A**, **B** provided only that the number of columns of **A** equals the number of rows of **B**. If **A** is an $m \times n$ matrix, and **B** an $n \times p$ matrix, then given any p-vector **u**, **Bu** is defined and is an n-vector, whence **A**(**Bu**) is defined and is an m-vector. This shows that the product $\mathbf{C} = \mathbf{AB}$ must be an $m \times p$ matrix (since it operates on a p-vector and the result is an m-vector). This relation is easily remembered if it is written thus:

$$\underset{m \times n}{\mathbf{A}} \cdot \underset{n \times p}{\mathbf{B}} = \underset{m \times p}{\mathbf{C}}. \qquad (11)$$

The laws written down previously for the addition and multiplication of matrices all apply to rectangular matrices whose dimensions are such that either side of the equation is defined. Here the fact that, in general, $\mathbf{AB} \neq \mathbf{BA}$ becomes even more obvious: **AB** may be defined without **BA** being defined and even when both **AB** and **BA** are defined, they need not have the same number of rows and columns (e.g. take **A** to be 2×3 and **B** 3×2).

Whereas the zero-matrix is defined for any number of rows and columns, the unit-matrix **I** is necessarily square, and if in the equations

$$\mathbf{IA} = \mathbf{AI} = \mathbf{A},$$

A is an $m \times n$ matrix, then the first **I** must be of order m and the second **I** of order n, if the equations are to have a meaning.[1] In cases of doubt, the order of any **I** occurring could be indicated by a suffix; the above equations would then read:

$$\mathbf{I}_m\mathbf{A} = \mathbf{A}\mathbf{I}_n = \mathbf{A}.$$

9. An extreme case of a rectangular matrix is a vector: a column-vector of dimension n may be considered as an $n \times 1$ matrix, and from this point of view the way in which a matrix operates on a column-vector (as in (2)) is just an instance of matrix-multiplication. The equation

$$\underset{m \times n}{\mathbf{A}} \ \underset{n \times 1}{\mathbf{x}} = \underset{m \times 1}{\mathbf{y}}$$

illustrates the rule (11). It also shows the advantage of writing vectors as columns (on the right of the matrix). For this leads us to adopt the 'row-by-column' rule of multiplication, which in turn is responsible for the very simple form of the associative law of multiplication (M.1).

Nevertheless row-vectors, that is, vectors written as horizontal rows, can also be fitted into this scheme. A row-vector of dimension n is a $1 \times n$ matrix and if we want to multiply it by an $n \times n$ matrix we have to put the vector on the left. E.g. for $n=2$, we could write

$$(x_1 \quad x_2)\begin{pmatrix} a & b \\ c & d \end{pmatrix} = (y_1 \quad y_2). \tag{12}$$

[1] The equations are true whenever they have a meaning; this may again be verified by the definition of the product **AB**.

This gives $y_1 = x_1a + x_2c$, $y_2 = x_1b + x_2d$, or, in matrix-form,

$$\begin{pmatrix} a & c \\ b & d \end{pmatrix}\begin{pmatrix} x_1 \\ x_2 \end{pmatrix} = \begin{pmatrix} y_1 \\ y_2 \end{pmatrix}. \qquad (13)$$

Thus the equation (12) between row-vectors is equivalent to the equation (13) between column-vectors. The square matrix in (12) appears again in (13), but with its columns written as rows and its rows written as columns. We call the operation of deriving a new matrix $\mathbf{A}'$ from $\mathbf{A}$ by taking for the columns of $\mathbf{A}'$ the rows of $\mathbf{A}$, *transposition* and call $\mathbf{A}'$ the *transpose* of $\mathbf{A}$. If $\mathbf{A}$ is an $m \times n$ matrix, its transpose $\mathbf{A}'$ is $n \times m$, e.g.

$$\mathbf{A} = \begin{pmatrix} 2 & 5 & -1 \\ 3 & 0 & 4 \end{pmatrix} \qquad \mathbf{A}' = \begin{pmatrix} 2 & 3 \\ 5 & 0 \\ -1 & 4 \end{pmatrix}.$$

In particular the transpose of a column-vector is the corresponding row-vector and vice-versa. We shall always denote the transpose of a matrix $\mathbf{A}$ by $\mathbf{A}'$; this agrees with the notation introduced in ch. II, where we wrote the column-vectors in the form $(x_1, \ldots, x_n)'$.

Let $\mathbf{A}$ be any matrix and let $\mathbf{A}'$ be its transpose. If we transpose $\mathbf{A}'$ we shall be taking the rows of $\mathbf{A}$ as rows and the columns of $\mathbf{A}$ as columns; in other words, the transpose of $\mathbf{A}'$ is just $\mathbf{A}$. In symbols

$$(\mathbf{A}')' = \mathbf{A}.$$

The rules for transposing sums and products are

T.1. $(\mathbf{A}+\mathbf{B})' = \mathbf{A}' + \mathbf{B}'$,
T.2. $(\lambda\mathbf{A})' = \lambda\mathbf{A}'$,
T.3. $(\mathbf{AB})' = \mathbf{B}'\mathbf{A}'$.

Of these rules T.1 and T.2 are immediate; T.3 follows by considering the (i,j)-element on both sides: on the left it is $\sum_k a_{jk}b_{ki}$, on the right it is $\sum_k b_{ki}a_{jk}$ and these two expressions are clearly equal. An illustration of T.3 is provided by a comparison of (12) and (13). If we write (13) as $\mathbf{Ax} = \mathbf{y}$, then (12) reads $\mathbf{x}'\mathbf{A}' = \mathbf{y}'$.

EXERCISES ON CHAPTER III

1. Verify M.1, 2, 3 for the following values of **A**, **B**, **C**, **D**:

(i)

$$\mathbf{A}=\begin{pmatrix}0&3\\4&5\end{pmatrix}\quad\mathbf{B}=\begin{pmatrix}2&-1\\3&2\end{pmatrix}\quad\mathbf{C}=\begin{pmatrix}1&4\\0&-2\end{pmatrix}\quad\mathbf{D}=\begin{pmatrix}-1&1\\2&-2\end{pmatrix}$$

(ii)

$$\mathbf{A}=\begin{pmatrix}1&-2&5\\3&0&4\end{pmatrix}\quad\mathbf{B}=\begin{pmatrix}2&1\\3&6\\1&5\end{pmatrix}\quad\mathbf{C}=\begin{pmatrix}3\\-3\end{pmatrix}\quad\mathbf{D}=\begin{pmatrix}1&3\\2&4\\-1&0\end{pmatrix}.$$

2. In which of the following cases are **AB** and **BA** (*a*) both defined, (*b*) of the same number of rows and columns, (*c*) equal?

(i) **A** and **B** as in 1.(i),

(ii) **A** and **B** as in 1.(ii),

(iii) $\mathbf{A}=\begin{pmatrix}2&-1\\3&2\end{pmatrix}\quad\mathbf{B}=\begin{pmatrix}1&-4\\12&1\end{pmatrix},$

(iv) $\mathbf{A}=\begin{pmatrix}3&1&-4\\-2&0&5\\1&-2&3\end{pmatrix}\quad\mathbf{B}=\begin{pmatrix}2&0&0\\0&5&0\\0&0&-1\end{pmatrix}.$

An example from everyday life of operations which can be performed in succession is the following: let **A** be the operation of putting a shoe on the right foot, and **B** the operation of putting a sock on the right foot; further let **AB** mean: first **B**, then **A**, and similarly **BA**, first **A** then **B**. Then we have $\mathbf{AB}\neq\mathbf{BA}$ (as may be verified experimentally). On the other hand, if **C** is the operation of putting a sock on the left foot, then $\mathbf{BC}=\mathbf{CB}$, $\mathbf{AC}=\mathbf{CA}$.

3. Expand $(\mathbf{A}-\mathbf{B})^2$ and check your expression by taking **A**, **B** as in 1(i).

4. Show that the matrix $\mathbf{A}=\begin{pmatrix}6&-4\\9&-6\end{pmatrix}$ satisfies the equation $\mathbf{A}^2=\mathbf{O}$, and find all 2×2 matrices satisfying this equation.

5. Evaluate $\mathbf{A}^2$, where $\mathbf{A}=\begin{pmatrix}2&-5\\3&1\end{pmatrix}$, and find scalars α, β, γ, not all zero, such that $\alpha\mathbf{I}+\beta\mathbf{A}+\gamma\mathbf{A}^2=\mathbf{O}$.

6. If **A** and **B** are $n \times n$ matrices and the columns of **B** are denoted by $\mathbf{b}_1, \ldots, \mathbf{b}_n$, show that the columns of **AB** are $\mathbf{Ab}_1, \ldots, \mathbf{Ab}_n$; in symbols,

$$\mathbf{A}(\mathbf{b}_1, \ldots, \mathbf{b}_n) = (\mathbf{Ab}_1, \ldots, \mathbf{Ab}_n).$$

7. Verify T.3 by taking **A**, **B** as in 1(i), 1(ii).

8. Show that for any matrix **A**, the products **AA**′ and **A**′**A** are defined, and evaluate **uu**′ and **u**′**u**, where $\mathbf{u} = (3, -2, 1, 4)'$.

9. Show that the rows of an $m \times n$ matrix **A** are $\mathbf{e}_i'\mathbf{A}$, where $\mathbf{e}_1, \ldots, \mathbf{e}_m$ is the basis of the space of m-vectors introduced in I.8.

CHAPTER FOUR

The Solution of a System of Equations: the General Case

1. In the case of the special systems of equations treated in ch. II, namely the regular systems, we saw that there was always just one solution, irrespective of the value of the right-hand side. In the general case this is not necessarily so: whether there is a solution at all, depends generally on the value of the right-hand side, and when there is a solution it need not be the only one.

Let us consider a general $m\times n$ system, written as

$$\mathbf{Ax}=\mathbf{k} \tag{I}$$

in the notation of ch. III. Here $\mathbf{A}$ is the $m\times n$ matrix of coefficients, $\mathbf{k}$ is a given m-vector, and we are looking for all n-vectors $\mathbf{x}$ which satisfy this equation.

The special case of (I) in which $\mathbf{k}=\mathbf{0}$,

$$\mathbf{Ax}=\mathbf{0}, \tag{H}$$

is called a *homogeneous system*. Every homogeneous system has at least one solution, namely the trivial solution $\mathbf{x}=\mathbf{0}$; it turns out to be a little easier to deal with than the general system (I) which may have no solution at all.

2. With any system (I) we associate the homogeneous system (H) obtained by replacing the right-hand side in (I) by $\mathbf{0}$. Then we have the following rules relating the solutions of (I) to the solutions of its associated homogeneous system (H):

(i) *If* $\mathbf{x}=\mathbf{v}_1$, $\mathbf{x}=\mathbf{v}_2$ *are any two solutions of* (I), *then* $\mathbf{x}=\mathbf{v}_1-\mathbf{v}_2$ *is a solution of* (H).

(ii) *If* $\mathbf{x}=\mathbf{u}$ *is a solution of* (H) and $\mathbf{x}=\mathbf{v}$ *is a solution of* (I), *then* $\mathbf{x}=\mathbf{u}+\mathbf{v}$ *is a solution of* (I).

These rules follow from equation (4) of III.3: If $\mathbf{Av}_1=\mathbf{Av}_2$

$=\mathbf{k}$, then $\mathbf{A}(\mathbf{v}_1-\mathbf{v}_2)=\mathbf{A}\mathbf{v}_1-\mathbf{A}\mathbf{v}_2=\mathbf{k}-\mathbf{k}=\mathbf{0}$; similarly, if $\mathbf{A}\mathbf{u}=\mathbf{0}$, $\mathbf{A}\mathbf{v}=\mathbf{k}$, then $\mathbf{A}(\mathbf{u}+\mathbf{v})=\mathbf{A}\mathbf{u}+\mathbf{A}\mathbf{v}=\mathbf{k}$.

Expressed in different terms, (i) states that any two solutions of (I) differ only by a solution of (H); therefore if we know a single solution of (I), we can find all solutions of (I) by adding to it the different solutions of (H). Rule (ii) states that when we add a solution of (H) to a solution of (I) we always do get a solution of (I). Thus in order to obtain the complete solution of (I) we need only know a single solution of (I) (if one exists), together with the most general solution of (H).

3. Before entering on the solution of (H) and (I) we shall restate the result of ch. II in matrix notation and derive an important consequence. The result as expressed in Theorem 1′ (ch. II.2) takes the following form:

If $\mathbf{A}$ *is a square matrix and if the equation* $\mathbf{A}\mathbf{x}=\mathbf{0}$ *has only the trivial solution* $\mathbf{x}=\mathbf{0}$, *then, for any* $\mathbf{k}$, *the equation* $\mathbf{A}\mathbf{x}=\mathbf{k}$ *has exactly one solution.*

Stated in this way, the result does not differ much from the one-dimensional case $ax=k$ discussed in the Introduction. This equation is regular if $ax=0$ has only the solution $x=0$, i.e. if $a\neq 0$; the solution is then $x=\frac{1}{a}.k$, or in a slightly different notation,

$$x=a^{-1}k.$$

We shall generalize this form of the solution by finding a matrix $\mathbf{A}^{-1}$, the 'inverse' of $\mathbf{A}$, such that the solution of the regular system $\mathbf{A}\mathbf{x}=\mathbf{k}$ takes the form $\mathbf{x}=\mathbf{A}^{-1}\mathbf{k}$.

Let us call a matrix $\mathbf{A}$ *regular* if it belongs to a regular system of equations, i.e. if $\mathbf{A}$ is square and $\mathbf{A}\mathbf{x}=\mathbf{0}$ has only the solution $\mathbf{x}=\mathbf{0}$. Now consider the equation

$$\mathbf{A}\mathbf{x}=\mathbf{e}_j,$$

where $\mathbf{A}$ is a regular matrix of order n and $\mathbf{e}_j$ is the j-th vector of the basis introduced in I.8. Since $\mathbf{A}$ is regular, this equation has a solution $\mathbf{b}_j=(b_{1j}, \ldots, b_{nj})'$, which is uniquely determined. If we determine $\mathbf{b}_j$ for $j=1, \ldots, n$, we have the equations

$$\mathbf{A}\mathbf{b}_j=\mathbf{e}_j \qquad (j=1, \ldots, n), \qquad (1)$$

which can also be expressed in the single matrix equation

$$\mathbf{AB}=\mathbf{I}, \tag{2}$$

where $\mathbf{B}=(b_{ij})$ is the matrix whose j-th column is $\mathbf{b}_j$. In fact (1) just states that the j-th columns on the two sides of (2) agree, for $j=1, \ldots, n$. With the help of $\mathbf{B}$ it is easy to solve the equation

$$\mathbf{Ax}=\mathbf{k}, \tag{3}$$

for any vector $\mathbf{k}$. For by (2), we have $\mathbf{A}(\mathbf{Bk})=(\mathbf{AB})\mathbf{k}=\mathbf{k}$, which shows that $\mathbf{Bk}$ is a solution of (3). When we take $\mathbf{k}=\mathbf{Ae}_j$, we see in this way that $\mathbf{x}=\mathbf{BAe}_j$ is a solution of the equation

$$\mathbf{Ax}=\mathbf{Ae}_j;$$

clearly this equation also has the solution $\mathbf{e}_j$, and since the solution is unique, we deduce that

$$\mathbf{BAe}_j=\mathbf{e}_j.$$

This equation holds for $j=1, \ldots, n$ and we can again sum up these equations by writing

$$\mathbf{BA}=\mathbf{I}. \tag{4}$$

We have now shown that for any regular matrix $\mathbf{A}$, there exists a matrix $\mathbf{B}$ such that

$$\mathbf{AB}=\mathbf{BA}=\mathbf{I}.$$

There can only be one such matrix, for if we also had $\mathbf{AC}=\mathbf{CA}=\mathbf{I}$, then $\mathbf{C}=\mathbf{C}(\mathbf{AB})=(\mathbf{CA})\mathbf{B}=\mathbf{B}$, which shows that $\mathbf{C}$ must equal $\mathbf{B}$. The matrix $\mathbf{B}$ determined in this way is called the *inverse* of $\mathbf{A}$ and is denoted by $\mathbf{A}^{-1}$. It corresponds to the inverse a^{-1} or $\frac{1}{a}$ of a non-zero scalar a. We state the result as

Theorem 3. *Every regular matrix* $\mathbf{A}$ *has a unique inverse* $\mathbf{A}^{-1}$ *satisfying* $\mathbf{A}^{-1}\mathbf{A}=\mathbf{AA}^{-1}=\mathbf{I}$.

Conversely, if for a given square matrix $\mathbf{A}$, the inverse $\mathbf{A}^{-1}$ exists, then $\mathbf{A}$ must be regular. For let $\mathbf{x}$ satisfy $\mathbf{Ax}=\mathbf{0}$, then $\mathbf{x}=\mathbf{A}^{-1}\mathbf{Ax}=\mathbf{0}$, which shows that $\mathbf{Ax}=\mathbf{0}$ has only the trivial solution and hence $\mathbf{A}$ is regular. It follows that a square matrix which is not regular has no inverse. Such a matrix (and the corresponding system of equations) is called *singular*. From the equations holding between a regular matrix $\mathbf{A}$ and its inverse $\mathbf{A}^{-1}$ (Theorem 3 above) it follows that $\mathbf{A}$ is the inverse of $\mathbf{A}^{-1}$. Hence $\mathbf{A}^{-1}$ is again regular and $(\mathbf{A}^{-1})^{-1}=\mathbf{A}$.

4. The construction of $\mathbf{A}^{-1}$ depended on the solution of the n vector equations $\mathbf{Ax}=\mathbf{e}_j$ $(j=1, \ldots, n)$. But there is no need to solve these n systems separately. We simply write down the scheme of coefficients of $\mathbf{A}$, and the n different columns representing the n different right-hand sides, and reduce these $2n$ columns simultaneously, as in ch. II. As an illustration we take a matrix which occurred already in II.8.

$$\mathbf{A}=\begin{pmatrix} 1 & 5 & 2 \\ 1 & 1 & 7 \\ 0 & -3 & 4 \end{pmatrix}.$$

We start from the scheme

$$\begin{array}{rrr|rrr} 1 & 5 & 2 & 1 & 0 & 0 \\ 1 & 1 & 7 & 0 & 1 & 0 \\ 0 & -3 & 4 & 0 & 0 & 1. \end{array}$$

If we operate on the rows of this scheme as in II.8, we obtain

$$\begin{array}{rrr|rrr} 1 & 5 & 2 & 1 & 0 & 0 \\ 1 & 1 & 7 & 0 & 1 & 0 \\ 0 & -3 & 4 & 0 & 0 & 1 \end{array} \quad R_2 \to R_2 - R_1 \quad \begin{array}{rrr|rrr} 1 & 5 & 2 & 1 & 0 & 0 \\ 0 & -4 & 5 & -1 & 1 & 0 \\ 0 & -3 & 4 & 0 & 0 & 1 \end{array}$$

$$R_2 \to R_2 - R_3 \quad \begin{array}{rrr|rrr} 1 & 5 & 2 & 1 & 0 & 0 \\ 0 & -1 & 1 & -1 & 1 & -1 \\ 0 & -3 & 4 & 0 & 0 & 1 \end{array} \quad R_2 \to -R_2$$

$$\begin{array}{rrr|rrr} 1 & 5 & 2 & 1 & 0 & 0 \\ 0 & 1 & -1 & 1 & -1 & 1 \\ 0 & -3 & 4 & 0 & 0 & 1 \end{array} \quad \begin{array}{l} R_1 \to R_1 - 5R_2 \\ R_3 \to R_3 + 3R_2 \end{array} \quad \begin{array}{rrr|rrr} 1 & 0 & 7 & -4 & 5 & -5 \\ 0 & 1 & -1 & 1 & -1 & 1 \\ 0 & 0 & 1 & 3 & -3 & 4 \end{array}$$

$$\begin{array}{l} R_1 \to R_1 - 7R_3 \\ R_2 \to R_2 + R_3 \end{array} \quad \begin{array}{rrr|rrr} 1 & 0 & 0 & -25 & 26 & -33 \\ 0 & 1 & 0 & 4 & -4 & 5 \\ 0 & 0 & 1 & 3 & -3 & 4. \end{array}$$

Thus

$$\mathbf{A}^{-1}=\begin{pmatrix} -25 & 26 & -33 \\ 4 & -4 & 5 \\ 3 & -3 & 4 \end{pmatrix}.$$

The process may be described as follows: If, by a series of steps of the form α, β or γ (cf. II.3), we can reduce the scheme $\mathbf{A} \mid \mathbf{I}$ to the scheme $\mathbf{I} \mid \mathbf{B}$, then $\mathbf{A}$ is regular and $\mathbf{B}=\mathbf{A}^{-1}$. The inverse steps are again of the form α, β or γ, and, performed in the opposite order, they lead from $\mathbf{I} \mid \mathbf{B}$ to $\mathbf{A} \mid \mathbf{I}$ or, what is the same, from $\mathbf{B} \mid \mathbf{I}$ to $\mathbf{I} \mid \mathbf{A}$. Hence $\mathbf{B}$ $(=\mathbf{A}^{-1})$ is also regular and $\mathbf{B}^{-1}=\mathbf{A}$. This shows again that if $\mathbf{A}$ is any regular matrix, $\mathbf{A}^{-1}$ is also regular and $(\mathbf{A}^{-1})^{-1}=\mathbf{A}$ (cf. IV.3).

5. As we have seen in No. 3, we can regard $\mathbf{A}^{-1}$ as a kind of universal solution, from which the solution of $\mathbf{Ax}=\mathbf{k}$ can be obtained, for any value of $\mathbf{k}$, by matrix multiplication. To illustrate this we can use the value of $\mathbf{A}^{-1}$ found above to solve the example treated in II.8. Here $\mathbf{k}=(9,6,-2)'$, and

$$\mathbf{A}^{-1}\mathbf{k}=\begin{pmatrix} -25 & 26 & -33 \\ 4 & -4 & 5 \\ 3 & -3 & 4 \end{pmatrix}\begin{pmatrix} 9 \\ 6 \\ -2 \end{pmatrix}=\begin{pmatrix} -3 \\ 2 \\ 1 \end{pmatrix},$$

which agrees with the solution found in II.8.

6. For any $m \times n$ matrix $\mathbf{A}$ we define the *rank* of $\mathbf{A}$ as the greatest number of columns of $\mathbf{A}$ which are linearly independent. By I.9 and II.11, to say that $\mathbf{A}$ has rank r is to say that the space spanned by the columns of $\mathbf{A}$ is of dimension r. E.g. if $\mathbf{a}_1, \ldots, \mathbf{a}_n$ are the columns of $\mathbf{A}$ and if the set $\mathbf{a}_1, \ldots, \mathbf{a}_r$ is linearly independent, but no larger set, then the rank of $\mathbf{A}$ is r. In this case it is possible to express each of the $\mathbf{a}_i$ linearly in terms of $\mathbf{a}_1, \ldots, \mathbf{a}_r$.

Similarly, the *rank* of the system of equations $\mathbf{Ax}=\mathbf{k}$ is defined as the rank of the matrix $\mathbf{A}$.

7. The basic fact about the solution of homogeneous systems is expressed by

Theorem 4. *Let*

$$\mathbf{Ax}=\mathbf{0} \tag{H}$$

be a homogeneous $m \times n$ system of rank r; then the solutions of *this system form a vector space of dimension* $n-r$. *That is, there exist linearly independent vectors* $\mathbf{c}_1, \ldots, \mathbf{c}_{n-r}$ *such that every linear combination of these* **c**'s *is a solution of* (H) *and conversely, every solution of* (H) *can be expressed as a linear combination of the* **c**'s.

To prove this theorem let us denote the columns of **A** by $\mathbf{a}_1, \ldots, \mathbf{a}_n$, so that the system becomes

$$\mathbf{a}_1x_1 + \ldots + \mathbf{a}_nx_n = \mathbf{0}. \tag{5}$$

The system is unchanged except for notation if we renumber the columns and the x_i in the same way; we may therefore suppose the columns numbered so that $\mathbf{a}_1, \ldots, \mathbf{a}_r$ are linearly independent, while $\mathbf{a}_{r+1}, \ldots, \mathbf{a}_n$ depend on $\mathbf{a}_1, \ldots, \mathbf{a}_r$, so that the equation

$$\mathbf{a}_1x_1 + \ldots + \mathbf{a}_rx_r = -\mathbf{a}_{r+i}$$

has a solution $(x_1, \ldots, x_r) = (c_{1i}, \ldots, c_{ri})$ say, for $i = 1, \ldots, n-r$. This means that the equation (5) has a solution $\mathbf{x} = \mathbf{c}_i$, where

$$\mathbf{c}_i = (c_{1i}, \ldots, c_{ri}, 0, 0, \ldots, 0, 1, 0, \ldots, 0)';$$

here the last $n-r$ coefficients are zero except for the $(r+i)$-th which is 1. We complete the proof by showing that every linear combination of the vectors $\mathbf{c}_1, \ldots, \mathbf{c}_{n-r}$ is a solution of (5), and conversely, every solution of (5) can be expressed uniquely[1] as a linear combination of these $n-r$ vectors.

In the first place we have, by construction, $\mathbf{Ac}_i = \mathbf{0}$, and hence, for any scalars λ_i,

$$\mathbf{A}(\Sigma\lambda_i\mathbf{c}_i) = \Sigma\lambda_i\mathbf{Ac}_i = \mathbf{0}.$$

Conversely, if $\mathbf{x} = \mathbf{u}$, where $\mathbf{u} = (u_1, \ldots, u_n)'$, is any solution of (5) then $\mathbf{x} = u_{r+1}\mathbf{c}_1 + \ldots + u_n\mathbf{c}_{n-r}$ is a solution of (5) whose last $n-r$ coordinates are $u_{r+1}, \ldots, u_n$, and it therefore agrees with **u** in these coordinates. In other words, the last $n-r$ coordinates of the difference

$$\mathbf{v} = \mathbf{u} - u_{r+1}\mathbf{c}_1 - \ldots - u_n\mathbf{c}_{n-r} \tag{6}$$

are zero. By the property (i) of homogeneous systems (cf. IV.2), $\mathbf{x} = \mathbf{v}$ is a solution of (5), i.e. if $\mathbf{v} = (v_1, \ldots, v_r, 0, \ldots, 0)'$, then

$$\mathbf{a}_1v_1 + \ldots + \mathbf{a}_rv_r = \mathbf{0}.$$

Since $\mathbf{a}_1, \ldots, \mathbf{a}_r$ are linearly independent, it follows that $v_1 = v_2 = \ldots = v_r = 0$. Thus the first r coordinates of **v** are zero as well, and we have

$$\mathbf{u} = u_{r+1}\mathbf{c}_1 + \ldots + u_n\mathbf{c}_{n-r}.$$

[1] The linear independence of the **c**'s follows from this uniqueness. Cf. I.7.

The coefficients in this equation are uniquely determined as the last $n-r$ components of $\mathbf{u}$. We have now shown that the solutions of (5) form a space with the basis $\mathbf{c}_1, \ldots, \mathbf{c}_{n-r}$, and this establishes the theorem.

In practice there is no need to find beforehand a maximal set of linearly independent columns. We simply carry out the reduction as in ch. II; it may not be possible now to eliminate unknowns in the natural order (corresponding to the fact that we have had to renumber the columns in the proof of Theorem 4), but this does not matter. In general we shall not have to solve for all the unknowns, since some of them can take arbitrary values. The process of elimination, applied to a homogeneous system of rank r, is complete when all but r equations have been reduced to 0 by subtracting multiples of other equations, and r of the columns, taken in a suitable order, form the $r \times r$ unit matrix. The unknowns corresponding to these r columns are then determined by the equations in terms of the remaining $n-r$ unknowns, whose values are arbitrary. In the proof of Theorem 4, these arbitrary or 'disposable' unknowns were $x_{r+1}, \ldots, x_n$.

8. We give two examples to illustrate the process of solving homogeneous systems:

$$\begin{aligned} 2x_1 + x_2 + 5x_3 &= 0 \\ x_1 - 3x_2 + 6x_3 &= 0 \\ 3x_1 + 5x_2 + 4x_3 &= 0 \\ 7x_2 - 7x_3 &= 0. \end{aligned}$$

If we write down the scheme of coefficients and the reductions as in ch. II, we have

$$\begin{matrix} 2 & 1 & 5 \\ 1 & -3 & 6 \\ 3 & 5 & 4 \\ 0 & 7 & -7 \end{matrix} \quad R_1 \longleftrightarrow R_2 \quad \begin{matrix} 1 & -3 & 6 \\ 2 & 1 & 5 \\ 3 & 5 & 4 \\ 0 & 7 & -7 \end{matrix} \quad \begin{matrix} \\ R_2 \to R_2 - 2R_1 \\ R_3 \to R_3 - 3R_1 \\ \\ \end{matrix} \quad \begin{matrix} 1 & -3 & 6 \\ 0 & 7 & -7 \\ 0 & 14 & -14 \\ 0 & 7 & -7 \end{matrix}$$

$$\begin{matrix} \\ R_3 \to R_3 - 2R_2 \\ R_4 \to R_4 - R_2 \\ \\ \end{matrix} \quad \begin{matrix} 1 & -3 & 6 \\ 0 & 7 & -7 \\ 0 & 0 & 0 \\ 0 & 0 & 0. \end{matrix}$$

At this stage we can discard the last two rows; they mean that the 3rd and 4th equation have been reduced to zero by subtracting multiples of the first two equations. In other words, equations 3 and 4 are linear combinations of equations 1 and 2, and so do not contribute to the solution.

We continue with

$$\begin{matrix} 1 & -3 & 6 \\ 0 & 7 & -7 \end{matrix} \quad R_2 \to \tfrac{1}{7}R_2 \quad \begin{matrix} 1 & -3 & 6 \\ 0 & 1 & -1 \end{matrix} \quad R_1 \to R_1 + 3R_2 \quad \begin{matrix} 1 & 0 & 3 \\ 0 & 1 & -1. \end{matrix}$$

We have now reached the stage described in No. 5: all but two of the rows have been reduced to zero, and two of the columns, taken in a suitable order, constitute the columns of the 2×2 unit-matrix.

The corresponding equations are

$$\begin{aligned} x_1 + 3x_3 &= 0 \\ x_2 - x_3 &= 0. \end{aligned}$$

The equations show that x_3 is disposable; its value determines the solution uniquely. If we denote the value of x_3 by λ, we obtain as the general solution

$$\begin{pmatrix} x_1 \\ x_2 \\ x_3 \end{pmatrix} = \begin{pmatrix} -3\lambda \\ \lambda \\ \lambda \end{pmatrix} = \lambda \begin{pmatrix} -3 \\ 1 \\ 1 \end{pmatrix}.$$

The solution contains one parameter, thus the space of solutions is 1-dimensional and $n-r=1$; since $n=3$, we deduce that the rank of the given system is 2. Of course we could see this already from the fact that two equations were left at the end (which would determine the values of the non-disposable unknowns).

As a second illustration we take a 3×4 system:

$$\begin{aligned} 4x_1 + 12x_2 - 7x_3 + 6x_4 &= 0 \\ x_1 + 3x_2 - 2x_3 + x_4 &= 0 \\ 3x_1 + 9x_2 - 2x_3 + 11x_4 &= 0. \end{aligned}$$

We have

$$\begin{matrix} 4 & 12 & -7 & 6 \\ 1 & 3 & -2 & 1 \\ 3 & 9 & -2 & 11 \end{matrix} \quad R_1 \longleftrightarrow R_2 \quad \begin{matrix} 1 & 3 & -2 & 1 \\ 4 & 12 & -7 & 6 \\ 3 & 9 & -2 & 11 \end{matrix} \quad \begin{matrix} R_2 \longrightarrow R_2 - 4R_1 \\ R_3 \longrightarrow R_3 - 3R_1 \end{matrix}$$

$$\begin{matrix} 1 & 3 & -2 & 1 \\ 0 & 0 & 1 & 2 \\ 0 & 0 & 4 & 8 \end{matrix} \quad \begin{matrix} R_1 \longrightarrow R_1 + 2R_2 \\ R_3 \longrightarrow R_3 - 4R_2 \end{matrix} \quad \begin{matrix} 1 & 3 & 0 & 5 \\ 0 & 0 & 1 & 2 \\ 0 & 0 & 0 & 0. \end{matrix}$$

The first column shows that x_1 is determined by the first equation, and the third column shows that x_3 is determined by the second equation. The third equation depends linearly on the first two, and x_2 and x_4 are disposable unknowns. Taking $x_2=\lambda$, $x_4=\mu$, we obtain as the complete solution

$$\begin{pmatrix} x_1 \\ x_2 \\ x_3 \\ x_4 \end{pmatrix} = \begin{pmatrix} -3\lambda-5\mu \\ \lambda \\ -2\mu \\ \mu \end{pmatrix} = \lambda \begin{pmatrix} -3 \\ 1 \\ 0 \\ 0 \end{pmatrix} + \mu \begin{pmatrix} -5 \\ 0 \\ -2 \\ 1 \end{pmatrix}.$$

9. Consider now the general system

$$\mathbf{Ax}=\mathbf{k}. \tag{I}$$

Let us denote the columns of $\mathbf{A}$ again by $\mathbf{a}_1, \ldots, \mathbf{a}_n$, and let us denote the $m \times (n+1)$ matrix with columns $\mathbf{a}_1, \ldots, \mathbf{a}_n, \mathbf{k}$ by $(\mathbf{A},\mathbf{k})$; this is sometimes called the *augmented matrix* of the system (I).

To solve the system (I) is to express $\mathbf{k}$ as a linear combination of $\mathbf{a}_1, \ldots, \mathbf{a}_n$ and this is possible if and only if $\mathbf{k}$ lies in the space spanned by $\mathbf{a}_1, \ldots, \mathbf{a}_n$, i.e. when the spaces spanned by $\mathbf{a}_1, \ldots, \mathbf{a}_n$ and $\mathbf{a}_1, \ldots, \mathbf{a}_n, \mathbf{k}$ respectively have the same dimension. In other words, (I) has a solution if and only if $\mathbf{A}$ and $(\mathbf{A},\mathbf{k})$ have the same rank. If we recall the connexion between the system (I) and its associated homogeneous system explained in No. 2, we can describe the nature of the solution of (I) as follows:

Theorem 5. *The* $m \times n$ *system*

$$\mathbf{Ax}=\mathbf{k} \tag{I}$$

has a solution if and only if the rank of its matrix **A** *equals the rank of the augmented matrix* (**A**,**k**). *If this rank is* r, *then the complete solution of (I) contains* $n-r$ *independent parameters, and is obtained by adding the general solution of the associated homogeneous system to a particular solution of (I).*

10. To solve the general system (I) in practice, we apply again the method of elimination, writing down the column on the right as well. We can carry out the reduction as in No. 6. If at any stage the left-hand side of an equation has been reduced to zero and the right-hand side is $\neq 0$, the system has no solution; if the right-hand side is zero too, the equation can be discarded. For a consistent[1] system of equations of rank r the process comes to an end when all but r equations have been discarded and among the columns of these equations there are r which constitute the different columns of the $r\times r$ unit-matrix (in a certain order). The corresponding unknowns are then determined by these r equations, while the remaining $n-r$ unknowns are disposable. Consider, e.g., the system

$$\begin{aligned} x_1-2x_2+5x_3&=1\\ 2x_1-4x_2+8x_3&=2\\ -3x_1+6x_2+7x_3&=1. \end{aligned} \tag{7}$$

We have

$$\left.\begin{array}{rrr|r} 1 & -2 & 5 & 1\\ 2 & -4 & 8 & 2\\ -3 & 6 & 7 & 1 \end{array}\right. \quad \begin{array}{l} R_2\rightarrow R_2-2R_1\\ R_3\rightarrow R_3+3R_1 \end{array} \quad \left.\begin{array}{rrr|r} 1 & -2 & 5 & 1\\ 0 & 0 & -2 & 0\\ 0 & 0 & 22 & 4 \end{array}\right. \quad R_2\rightarrow -\tfrac{1}{2}R_2$$

$$\left.\begin{array}{rrr|r} 1 & -2 & 5 & 1\\ 0 & 0 & 1 & 0\\ 0 & 0 & 22 & 4 \end{array}\right. \quad \begin{array}{l} R_1\rightarrow R_1-5R_2\\ R_3\rightarrow R_3-22R_2 \end{array} \quad \left.\begin{array}{rrr|r} 1 & -2 & 0 & 1\\ 0 & 0 & 1 & 0\\ 0 & 0 & 0 & 4. \end{array}\right.$$

The system has no solution, since the last equation now reads

$$0=4.$$

If in (7), the right-hand side had been $(1, 2, -3)'$, we would

[1] By a *consistent* system we mean a system which has at least one solution.

have found (with the same operations on the schemes as above)

$$\begin{array}{rrr|r} 1 & -2 & 5 & 1 \\ 2 & -4 & 8 & 2 \\ -3 & 6 & 7 & -3 \end{array} \quad \begin{array}{rrr|r} 1 & -2 & 5 & 1 \\ 0 & 0 & -2 & 0 \\ 0 & 0 & 22 & 0 \end{array} \quad \begin{array}{rrr|r} 1 & -2 & 5 & 1 \\ 0 & 0 & 1 & 0 \\ 0 & 0 & 22 & 0 \end{array} \quad \begin{array}{rrr|r} 1 & -2 & 0 & 1 \\ 0 & 0 & 1 & 0 \\ 0 & 0 & 0 & 0. \end{array}$$

From the last scheme we obtain

$$\begin{aligned} x_1 - 2x_2 &= 1 \\ x_3 &= 0. \end{aligned}$$

This is a consistent system of rank 2, with x_2 as the disposable unknown. Thus the solution is

$$\begin{pmatrix} x_1 \\ x_2 \\ x_3 \end{pmatrix} = \begin{pmatrix} 1 \\ 0 \\ 0 \end{pmatrix} + \lambda \begin{pmatrix} 2 \\ 1 \\ 0 \end{pmatrix}.$$

We see that $(1, 0, 0)'$ is a particular solution, while $\lambda(2, 1, 0)'$ is the general solution of the associated homogeneous system.

11. When the equations are in 2 or 3 unknowns, we can give them a geometrical interpretation by taking the unknowns to be coordinates in the plane or in space. For the case of the plane there are essentially 3 possibilities, corresponding to the 3 examples given in the Introduction. In 3 dimensions there are more possibilities, since the rank of the system may now be 0, 1, 2 or 3.

All we have to assume from solid coordinate geometry is the fact that the equation

$$a_1x_1 + a_2x_2 + a_3x_3 = k,$$

where a_1, a_2, a_3 are not all zero, represents a plane (in a coordinate system with coordinates x_1, x_2 and x_3). This is analogous to the statement that in two dimensions the equation $a_1x_1 + a_2x_2 = k$, where a_1 and a_2 are not both zero, represents a straight line.

Let us take a 3×3 system

$$\mathbf{Ax} = \mathbf{k}, \tag{8}$$

in which none of the rows of $\mathbf{A}$ is zero, so that the 3 equations of the system (8) represent 3 planes in space. These 3 planes may intersect in a point, a line, a plane or not at all, and the coordinates of all the points of intersection are plainly just the solutions $(x_1, x_2, x_3)'$ of (8). We now indicate the possibilities briefly in terms of the ranks of $\mathbf{A}$ and of the augmented matrix $(\mathbf{A}, \mathbf{k})$. The rank of

A can have 3 different values, 1, 2 or 3 (it cannot be 0, because **A** is not the zero-matrix). The rank of (**A**, **k**) is either equal to this value or exceeds it by 1; it cannot exceed the rank of **A** by more than 1 because we have only one more column at our disposal in (**A**, **k**).

1. rank(**A**) = rank(**A**,**k**) = 3. The equations have a unique solution, and hence the planes intersect in a single point (Fig. 5).

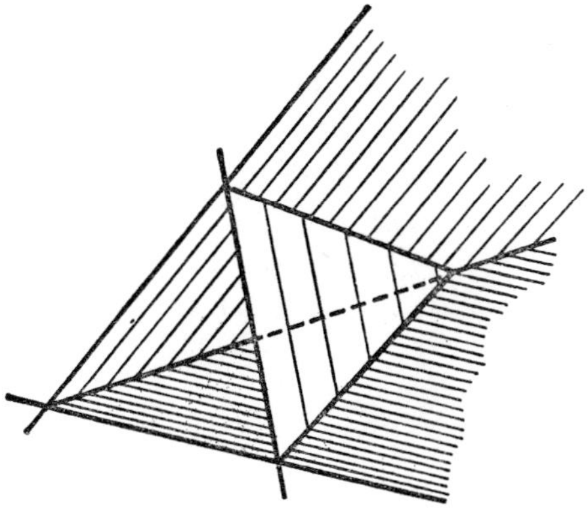

FIG. 5.

2a. rank(**A**) = rank(**A**,**k**) = 2. The equations have a solution and the general solution depends on one parameter. The 3 planes intersect in a line (Fig. 6).

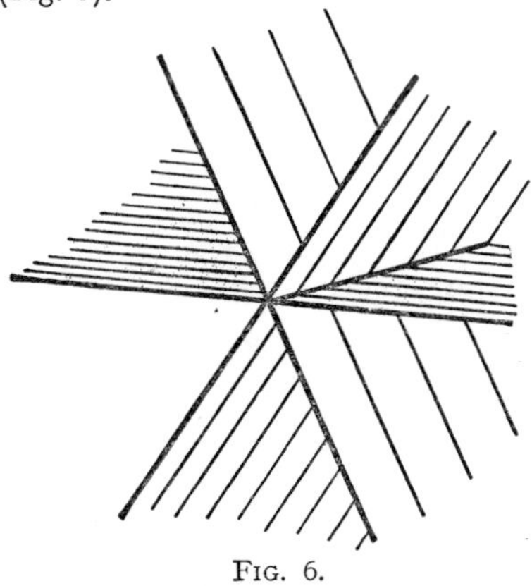

FIG. 6.

2*b*. rank($\mathbf{A}$) = 2, rank($\mathbf{A},\mathbf{k}$) = 3. The equations have no solution. The planes are parallel to the same straight line, but have no common point (Fig. 7).

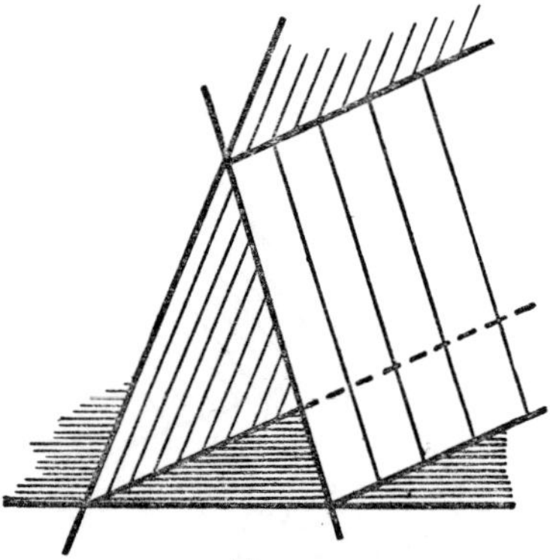

FIG. 7.

3*a*. rank($\mathbf{A}$) = rank($\mathbf{A},\mathbf{k}$) = 1. Only one equation remains after elimination; hence the 3 equations are proportional in this case, and so they represent the same plane. Thus the 3 planes coincide.

3*b*. rank($\mathbf{A}$) = 1, rank($\mathbf{A},\mathbf{k}$) = 2. The 3 planes are parallel, but do not all coincide.

EXERCISES ON CHAPTER IV

1. Find the inverse of each of the matrices belonging to the systems in ex. 1 (i)–(viii) of ch. II.

2. Prove that any regular matrix $\mathbf{A}$ satisfies $(\mathbf{A}^{-1})' = (\mathbf{A}')^{-1}$. Verify this rule by taking for $\mathbf{A}$ a matrix from ex. 1. (Hint: Transpose the equations relating $\mathbf{A}$ and $\mathbf{A}^{-1}$ (Theorem 3) and use the uniqueness of $\mathbf{A}^{-1}$.)

3. Prove that any two regular matrices $\mathbf{A}$, $\mathbf{B}$ of the same order satisfy the equation $(\mathbf{AB})^{-1} = \mathbf{B}^{-1}\mathbf{A}^{-1}$. Verify this result by taking for $\mathbf{A}$ and $\mathbf{B}$ pairs of matrices of the same order from ex. 1. (This result is of general validity for any two operations $\mathbf{A}$, $\mathbf{B}$ which can be performed in succession and which have

inverses. A practical illustration may be obtained by taking **A** and **B** as in the remark to ex. 2 of ch. III.)

4. Prove the following rule (sometimes known as the principle of superposition): If $\mathbf{x}=\mathbf{v}_1$ is a solution of $\mathbf{Ax}=\mathbf{k}_1$ and $\mathbf{x}=\mathbf{v}_2$ is a solution of $\mathbf{Ax}=\mathbf{k}_2$, and λ_1, λ_2 are any scalars, then $\mathbf{x}=\lambda_1\mathbf{v}_1+\lambda_2\mathbf{v}_2$ is a solution of $\mathbf{Ax}=\lambda_1\mathbf{k}_1+\lambda_2\mathbf{k}_2$.

5. What are the possible values for the rank of the matrix $\mathbf{uu}'$, where $\mathbf{u}$ is a column-vector?

6. Adapt the method of IV.4 to calculate $\mathbf{A}^{-1}\mathbf{B}$, where **A** and **B** are square matrices of the same order. Find a similar method for $\mathbf{BA}^{-1}$. (Hint: to obtain $\mathbf{A}^{-1}\mathbf{B}$, reduce the scheme $\mathbf{A} \mid \mathbf{B}$ by elementary operations until the matrix on the left of the bar is the unit-matrix. For $\mathbf{BA}^{-1}$ start from $\mathbf{A}' \mid \mathbf{B}'$ and transpose the result.)

7. Show that an $(m+1)\times m$ homogeneous system always has a non-trivial solution. (Hint: Use Theorem 2, II.10.)

8. Show that an $m\times n$ system of rank m always has a solution. (Hint: Use Theorem 2, II.10.)

9. The following schemes represent systems of equations in the notation of II.8. Find the complete solution in the cases where there is one:

$$\text{(i)}\ \begin{array}{ccc|c} 2 & 4 & 1 & 1 \\ 3 & 5 & 0 & 1 \\ 5 & 13 & 7 & 4 \end{array} \qquad \text{(ii)}\ \begin{array}{ccc|c} 9 & -6 & 12 & 0 \\ -12 & 8 & -16 & 0 \\ -7 & 10 & -13 & 0 \end{array} \qquad \text{(iii)}\ \begin{array}{ccc|c} 2 & 3 & 4 & 1 \\ 5 & 6 & 7 & 2 \\ 8 & 9 & 10 & 4 \end{array}$$

$$\text{(iv)}\ \begin{array}{cccc|c} 2 & 1 & 3 & 5 & 6 \\ 3 & 2 & 4 & 6 & 8 \\ -1 & 3 & 2 & 7 & -3 \end{array} \qquad \text{(v)}\ \begin{array}{cccc|c} 3 & 1 & -2 & -1 & 2 \\ 15 & 5 & 4 & 3 & 4 \\ 6 & 2 & 3 & 1 & 0 \end{array}$$

$$\text{(vi)}\ \begin{array}{cccc|c} 1 & -3 & 5 & -7 & -2 \\ -2 & 4 & -6 & 8 & 2 \\ 1 & 1 & 1 & 1 & 2 \\ 1 & 5 & 2 & 5 & 7 \end{array} \qquad \text{(vii)}\ \begin{array}{cccc|c} 3 & 1 & 2 & 4 & 3 \\ 5 & 2 & 3 & 6 & 5 \\ 4 & 1 & 3 & 6 & 4 \\ 5 & 1 & 4 & 8 & 5. \end{array}$$

10. In the following schemes, determine all the values of t for

which there is a solution, and give the complete solution in each case:

$$\text{(i)}\quad \begin{array}{rrrr|l} 1 & 4 & -2 & 3 & t \\ 3 & 5 & 0 & 2 & 5 \\ 0 & 7 & -6 & 7 & 13 \end{array} \qquad \text{(ii)}\quad \begin{array}{rrrr|l} 2 & 1 & 4 & 3 & 1 \\ 1 & 3 & 2 & -1 & 3t \\ 1 & 1 & 2 & 1 & t^2. \end{array}$$

(iii) Determine t so that the system represented by the scheme

$$\begin{array}{rrr|l} 2 & 2 & 3 & 0 \\ 3 & t & 5 & 0 \\ 1 & 7 & 3 & 0 \end{array}$$

has a non-trivial solution, and then solve it completely.

CHAPTER FIVE

Determinants

1. In the preceding chapter we described the form taken by the solution of an $m \times n$ system of equations. The form of this solution depended essentially on the *rank* of the system, that is the maximum number of linearly independent columns; but since the process of solving the equations also provided the value of the rank, we did not need any special methods for determining the rank. In fact almost every method for determining the rank of a system is similar (and comparable in length) to the method of solving the equations given in chapters II and IV. Nevertheless it is often useful to have another characterization of the rank, and in particular, to have a criterion for the linear dependence of n vectors in n dimensions.

2. Let us first consider the case of 2-vectors. If the vectors $\mathbf{u}=(u_1, u_2)'$ and $\mathbf{v}=(v_1, v_2)'$ are linearly dependent then there exist two scalars λ, μ, not both zero, such that

$$\begin{aligned} \lambda u_1+\mu v_1&=0 \\ \lambda u_2+\mu v_2&=0. \end{aligned} \tag{1}$$

Eliminating μ and λ in turn, we find that

$$\begin{aligned} \lambda(u_1v_2-u_2v_1)&=0 \\ \mu(u_1v_2-u_2v_1)&=0; \end{aligned}$$

since one of λ, μ is $\neq 0$, we conclude that

$$u_1v_2-u_2v_1=0. \tag{2}$$

Conversely, if (2) holds then $\mathbf{u}$ and $\mathbf{v}$ are linearly dependent. For, either $\mathbf{u}=\mathbf{0}$ and so (1) holds with $\lambda=1$, $\mu=0$; or one of u_1, u_2 is $\neq 0$, say $u_1 \neq 0$. Then (1) holds with $\lambda=v_1$, $\mu=-u_1$.

Thus the function $\Delta=u_1v_2-u_2v_1$ of the components of $\mathbf{u}$ and $\mathbf{v}$ vanishes if and only if $\mathbf{u}$ and $\mathbf{v}$ are linearly dependent. It is called a *determinant* of order 2, and is denoted by

$$\begin{vmatrix} u_1 & v_1 \\ u_2 & v_2 \end{vmatrix}. \tag{3}$$

The determinant (3) may be interpreted geometrically as twice the area of the triangle with the vertices (0, 0), (u_1, u_2) and (v_1, v_2), with a sign depending on the order in which these points are taken.

3. Let us now take three vectors **u**, **v**, **w** in three dimensions. If they are linearly dependent, then there exist λ, μ, ν, not all zero, such that

$$\begin{aligned} \lambda u_1+\mu v_1+\nu w_1&=0 \\ \lambda u_2+\mu v_2+\nu w_2&=0 \\ \lambda u_3+\mu v_3+\nu w_3&=0. \end{aligned}$$

Eliminating μ and ν, we find

$$\lambda(u_1v_2w_3-u_1v_3w_2-u_2v_1w_3+u_2v_3w_1+u_3v_1w_2-u_3v_2w_1)=0;$$

if instead we eliminate λ and ν, or λ and μ, we obtain the same equation, with λ replaced by μ or ν respectively. Since at least one of λ, μ, ν is $\neq 0$, we conclude that

$$u_1v_2w_3-u_1v_3w_2-u_2v_1w_3+u_2v_3w_1+u_3v_1w_2-u_3v_2w_1=0.$$

The expression on the left is written

$$\begin{vmatrix} u_1 & v_1 & w_1 \\ u_2 & v_2 & w_2 \\ u_3 & v_3 & w_3 \end{vmatrix}$$

and is known as a determinant of order 3.

It can again be shown that this determinant vanishes if and only if **u**, **v** and **w** are linearly dependent; further it represents 6 times the volume of the tetrahedron with the vertices given by the vectors **0**, **u**, **v** and **w**.

4. The preceding cases suggest that there is a function of the components of n vectors (of dimension n) whose vanishing expresses the linear dependence of these vectors. In order to

define such a function we look again at the definition of a 3rd order determinant

$$u_1v_2w_3-u_1v_3w_2-u_2v_1w_3+u_2v_3w_1+u_3v_1w_2-u_3v_2w_1. \qquad (4)$$

It is a sum of terms $\pm u_iv_jw_k$, where i, j, k represent the numbers 1, 2, 3 in some order, and the sign is + or −, depending on that order. More precisely, the sign is + when ijk are in the order 123, 231, 312, and − when the order is 132, 321 or 213.

Each arrangement ijk of 123 can be obtained from 123 by successively interchanging certain pairs of numbers. E.g. we get from 123 to 231 by first interchanging 1,2 : 213, and then 1,3 : 231. This can be done in many different ways and the number of interchanges[1] need not be the same each time; thus we can get also from 123 to 231 using four interchanges instead of two: 123→213→312→321→231. But whatever route we use to get from 123 to 231, the number of interchanges will always be even. And if we can get from 123 to ijk by an odd number of interchanges then any method of getting from 123 to ijk by interchanges will involve an odd number of interchanges.

The rule of signs in (4) can now be expressed very simply as follows: $u_iv_jw_k$ appears in (4) with the sign + if ijk differs from 123 by an even number of interchanges, and with the sign − if ijk differs from 123 by an odd number of interchanges.

5. It is worth pausing briefly to examine the possible arrangements of n distinct numbers, and their division into two classes, as this will help us to understand the general definition of a determinant of order n.

The numbers 1, 2, . . . , n can be arranged in $n!$ different ways[2]; the operation by which we pass from 123 . . . n to any one of these arrangements, say $i_1i_2i_3 \ldots i_n$, is called a *permutation*.[3] We can always carry out such a permutation by interchanges of pairs of numbers.

[1] The interchange of two numbers in an arrangement is usually called a *transposition*. We shall not follow this usage to avoid confusion with the term as applied to matrices.

[2] $n!$ stands for 1.2.3. . . . .n; it is also sometimes denoted by $\underline{|n}$.

[3] This is the standard usage in mathematics. Unfortunately the usage in elementary mathematics is slightly different; here a 'permutation'

For $n=2$ this is clear since there are only 2 numbers present. In the general case we use induction (see II.7): We can bring i_1 to the first position by interchanging it with 1; of course if $i_1=1$, this is not necessary. Having brought i_1 to its correct position, we need only apply a permutation to the remaining $n-1$ numbers, and by our induction hypothesis we can do this by means of interchanges. Thus every permutation can be effected by a succession of interchanges.

Example: To get from 12345 to 31542 we have

$$12345 \rightarrow 32145 \rightarrow 31245 \rightarrow 31542.$$

There are of course other ways of expressing the permutation in terms of interchanges, but whether the number of interchanges used is even or odd depends only on the permutation and not on the way it is expressed.

To prove this assertion we take n variables $x_1, x_2, \ldots, x_n$ and form the product of their differences

$$\phi = \begin{cases} (x_1-x_2)(x_1-x_3)(x_1-x_4)\ldots(x_1-x_n) \\ \qquad\quad (x_2-x_3)(x_2-x_4)\ldots(x_2-x_n) \\ \qquad\qquad\quad \cdot\ \cdot\ \cdot \qquad \cdots \quad \cdot\ \cdot \\ \qquad\qquad\quad \cdot\ \cdot\ \cdot \qquad \cdots \quad \cdot\ \cdot \\ \qquad\qquad\qquad\qquad\qquad\qquad (x_{n-1}-x_n). \end{cases}$$

When we interchange x_1 and x_2, only the first two rows in this product are affected and it is easily seen that ϕ changes sign. Generally, the interchange of a pair of variables changes the sign of ϕ. If we apply k interchanges, ϕ is multiplied by $(-1)^k$ and this is 1 if k is even and -1 if k is odd. Since a permutation can always be effected by a succession of interchanges, any permutation, applied to $x_1, \ldots, x_n$, transforms ϕ into ϕ or $-\phi$. Of these two possibilities only one is realized, because $\phi \neq -\phi$. In the first case the number of interchanges is necessarily even, in the second case it is odd.

6. We shall call a permutation *even* or *odd*, according as the

means an arrangement of numbers in a given order, rather than a re-arrangement. Football pools give yet another meaning to the word: A 'permutation' or 'perm' is usually a choice of a specific set of teams without regard to their order, in other words, it is a 'combination'.

number of interchanges needed to effect the permutation is even or odd. Further we shall write

$$\varepsilon(i_1 i_2 \dots i_n) = \begin{cases} 1 \text{ if } i_1 i_2 \dots i_n \text{ is obtained from } 12 \dots n \text{ by} \\ \qquad \text{an even permutation,} \\ -1 \text{ if } i_1 i_2 \dots i_n \text{ is obtained from } 12 \dots n \text{ by} \\ \qquad \text{an odd permutation.} \end{cases}$$

The expression $\varepsilon(i_1 i_2 \dots i_n)$ so defined is known as the *Kronecker ε-symbol*. To calculate ε we simply reduce $i_1 i_2 \dots i_n$ to $12 \dots n$ by interchanges, changing the sign each time, and remember that $\varepsilon(12 \dots n) = 1$. E.g.

$$\varepsilon(31542) = -\varepsilon(31245) = \varepsilon(32145) = -\varepsilon(12345) = -1.$$

We note the following properties of the ε-symbol:

E.1. *If $j_1 j_2 \dots j_n$ differs from $i_1 i_2 \dots i_n$ by a single interchange, then $\varepsilon(j_1 j_2 \dots j_n) = -\varepsilon(i_1 i_2 \dots i_n)$. E.g.*

$$\varepsilon(i_2 i_1 i_3 \dots i_n) = -\varepsilon(i_1 i_2 i_3 \dots i_n).$$

E.2. *If $i_1 i_2 \dots i_n$ is obtained by a permutation of $12 \dots n$ and the permutation which takes $i_1 i_2 \dots i_n$ to $12 \dots n$, takes $12 \dots n$ to $j_1 j_2 \dots j_n$, then*

$$\varepsilon(j_1 j_2 \dots j_n) = \varepsilon(i_1 i_2 \dots i_n).$$

E.3. *If $i_2 i_3 \dots i_n$ is obtained by a permutation of $23 \dots n$, then*

$$\varepsilon(1 i_2 i_3 \dots i_n) = \varepsilon(i_2 i_3 \dots i_n).$$

Rule E.1 is obvious: if the two arrangements $i_1 i_2 \dots i_n$ and $j_1 j_2 \dots j_n$ differ by one interchange their ε-symbols must have opposite signs. To prove E.2 we observe that it takes as many interchanges to get from $12 \dots n$ to $i_1 i_2 \dots i_n$ as it does to get from $i_1 i_2 \dots i_n$ to $12 \dots n$. Therefore we can get from $12 \dots n$ to $i_1 i_2 \dots i_n$ and to $j_1 j_2 \dots j_n$ in the same number of interchanges. As an illustration to E.2, we get from 31542 to 12345 by the interchanges (25), (12), (13). If we apply these interchanges to 12345, we get successively 12345→15342→25341 →25143. Hence, by E.2, $\varepsilon(25143) = \varepsilon(31542)$.

Rule E.3 offers no difficulty: we have to apply a permutation to $1 i_2 i_3 \dots i_n$, and since 1 is in position, we need only use a permutation which sends $i_2 i_3 \dots i_n$ into $23 \dots n$.

7. To illustrate the use of the ε-symbols, we can define the determinant of order 3, formed from the components of the vectors **u**, **v**, **w** as $\Sigma\varepsilon(ijk)u_i v_j w_k$. In this summation ijk runs over the 6 arrangements of 123. When we expand and substitute the values of ε, namely $\varepsilon(123)=\varepsilon(231)=\varepsilon(312)=1$, $\varepsilon(132)=\varepsilon(321)=\varepsilon(213)=-1$, we just obtain (4). If for the 3 vectors we take the columns of a 3×3 matrix $\mathbf{A}=(a_{ij})$, the expression for the determinant of **A** reads

$$\Sigma\varepsilon(ijk)a_{i1}a_{j2}a_{k3}.$$

In analogy with this formula we define the determinant of an $n\times n$ matrix $\mathbf{A}=(a_{ij})$ as

$$\Sigma\varepsilon(i_1 i_2 \ldots i_n)a_{i_1 1}a_{i_2 2}\ldots a_{i_n n}, \tag{5}$$

where the summation is taken over the $n!$ arrangements $i_1 i_2 \ldots i_n$ of $12 \ldots n$. This expression (5) is known as a *determinant* of order n; it is written $|\mathbf{A}|$, or *det* **A** or, in full,

$$\begin{vmatrix} a_{11} & a_{12} \ldots & a_{1n} \\ a_{21} & a_{22} \ldots & a_{2n} \\ \cdot & \cdot \;\ldots & \cdot \\ a_{n1} & a_{n2} \ldots & a_{nn} \end{vmatrix}.$$

8. Let us consider the definition (5) for a moment. Clearly it generalizes the definition of 2nd and 3rd order determinants given previously. Since there are $n!$ arrangements of $12 \ldots n$, the expression (5) consists of $n!$ terms; any one includes just one element from each row and one element from each column.[1] For example, in any term containing a_{12}, there are also $n-1$ other factors a_{ij}, which come from rows other than the first and columns other than the second. If we collect the terms containing a_{12}, we can write their sum as $a_{12}A_{12}$, where A_{12}, the *cofactor* of a_{12}, is a certain expression in the a_{ij}, which contains no elements from the first row or the second column of A. In an analogous way we can define the cofactor A_{ij} of any element a_{ij}.

Let us now fix a row, say the first row. Since each non-zero

[1] Thus each term in the expression of an 8th order determinant corresponds to a distribution of 8 rooks on a chess-board in such a way that none can take any of the others.

term in (5) contains just one element from the first row, every such term will occur exactly once in one of the expressions $a_{1j}A_{1j}(j=1, \ldots, n)$, and we can therefore express the determinant as

$$a_{11}A_{11}+a_{12}A_{12}+\ldots+a_{1n}A_{1n},$$

with the cofactors as coefficients. This is called the expansion of $|\mathbf{A}|$ by its first row. We can expand $|\mathbf{A}|$ by any of its rows in this way: the result is

$$a_{i1}A_{i1}+a_{i2}A_{i2}+\ldots+a_{in}A_{in}=|\mathbf{A}| \quad (i=1, \ldots, n). \tag{6}$$

As an example we give the expansion of a 3rd order determinant by its first row:

$$\begin{vmatrix} a_{11} & a_{12} & a_{13} \\ a_{21} & a_{22} & a_{23} \\ a_{31} & a_{32} & a_{33} \end{vmatrix} = a_{11}(a_{22}a_{33}-a_{32}a_{23})+a_{12}(-a_{21}a_{33}+a_{31}a_{23}) \\ +a_{13}(a_{21}a_{32}-a_{31}a_{22}).$$

We notice that the cofactors in this expansion have the form of 2nd order determinants. In the general case we shall see that the cofactors can be expressed as determinants of order $n-1$.

We can also expand $|\mathbf{A}|$ by one of its columns, using the fact that each term of (5) contains just one element from any given column. Thus the expansion by the j-th column is

$$a_{1j}A_{1j}+a_{2j}A_{2j}+\ldots+a_{nj}A_{nj}=|\mathbf{A}|, \tag{7}$$

where the coefficients are again the cofactors.

9. We now list the most important properties of determinants.

D.1. *The determinant of a square matrix* $\mathbf{A}$ *is a linear function of the elements of any column of* $\mathbf{A}$.

This means that for any n-vectors $\mathbf{b}, \mathbf{a}_1, \mathbf{a}_2, \ldots, \mathbf{a}_n$, and any scalars λ, μ,

$$|\lambda\mathbf{a}_1+\mu\mathbf{b}, \mathbf{a}_2, \ldots, \mathbf{a}_n|=\lambda|\mathbf{a}_1, \mathbf{a}_2, \ldots, \mathbf{a}_n|+\mu|\mathbf{b}, \mathbf{a}_2, \ldots, \mathbf{a}_n|,$$

and similarly for the other columns.

D.2. *The determinant changes sign if two columns are interchanged; it is zero if two columns are the same.*

D.3. *The determinant is unchanged if a multiple of one column is added to another column.*

D.4. *The determinant remains unchanged if the columns are written as rows, in symbols*

$$|\mathbf{A}'|=|\mathbf{A}|.$$

If we apply D.4 to D.1–3, we obtain

D.1′–3′. *Rules* D.1–3 *apply when 'column' is replaced by 'row'.*

Rule D.1 is a consequence of equation (7), which expresses $|\mathbf{A}|$ as a linear function of the j-th column ($j=1, \ldots, n$). As an illustration,

$$\begin{vmatrix} \lambda a & \lambda b \\ \lambda c & \lambda d \end{vmatrix} = \lambda \begin{vmatrix} a & \lambda b \\ c & \lambda d \end{vmatrix} = \lambda^2 \begin{vmatrix} a & b \\ c & d \end{vmatrix}.$$

In particular, a determinant vanishes if any column is the zero-column. We note that D.1 may be used to express the determinant of a sum of two matrices $\mathbf{A}$ and $\mathbf{B}$ as a sum of 2^n determinants, the general determinant of this sum being formed by taking any number r of columns from $\mathbf{A}$ and the remaining $n-r$ columns from $\mathbf{B}$.[1]

Now consider D.2. If we interchange the first two columns, we obtain

$$\Sigma\varepsilon(i_1 i_2 \ldots i_n) a_{i_1 2} a_{i_2 1} a_{i_3 3} \ldots a_{j_n n}.$$

Put $j_2=i_1$, $j_1=i_2$, $j_\nu=i_\nu (\nu=3, \ldots, n)$, then the expression becomes

$$\begin{aligned} &\Sigma\varepsilon(j_2 j_1 j_3 \ldots j_n) a_{j_2 2} a_{j_1 1} a_{j_3 3} \ldots a_{j_n n} \\ &\qquad = -\Sigma\varepsilon(j_1 j_2 \ldots j_n) a_{j_1 1} a_{j_2 2} \ldots a_{j_n n} \quad \text{(by E.1)} \\ &\qquad = -|\mathbf{A}|; \end{aligned}$$

generally the interchange of any pair of columns changes the sign of $|\mathbf{A}|$. If two columns are the same, say if $\mathbf{a}_2=\mathbf{a}_1$, then

$$|\mathbf{A}|=|\mathbf{a}_1, \mathbf{a}_1, \mathbf{a}_3, \ldots, \mathbf{a}_n|=-|\mathbf{a}_1, \mathbf{a}_1, \mathbf{a}_3, \ldots, \mathbf{a}_n|,$$

by interchanging the first two columns. Hence $2|\mathbf{A}|=0$, i.e. $|\mathbf{A}|=0$. The same reasoning applies when another pair of columns agree.

D.3 is a consequence of D.1–2: consider, e.g., the case where a multiple of the second column is added to the first column.

[1] Note that $|\mathbf{A}+\mathbf{B}|\neq|\mathbf{A}|+|\mathbf{B}|$ in general.

The new determinant is

$$|\mathbf{a}_1+\lambda\mathbf{a}_2, \mathbf{a}_2, \mathbf{a}_3, \ldots, \mathbf{a}_n|=|\mathbf{a}_1, \mathbf{a}_2, \ldots, \mathbf{a}_n| +\lambda|\mathbf{a}_2, \mathbf{a}_2, \mathbf{a}_3, \ldots, \mathbf{a}_n| \quad \text{by D.1,}$$

$$=|\mathbf{a}_1, \mathbf{a}_2, \ldots, \mathbf{a}_n| \quad \text{by D.2.}$$

To prove D.4 we use E.2. When we apply a permutation to change $i_1i_2 \ldots i_n$ to $12 \ldots n$, $12 \ldots n$ will change to $j_1j_2 \ldots j_n$, say, and we can therefore write (6) as

$$\Sigma\varepsilon(i_1i_2 \ldots i_n)a_{1j_1}a_{2j_2} \ldots a_{nj_n};$$

by E.2, we have $\varepsilon(i_1i_2 \ldots i_n)=\varepsilon(j_1j_2 \ldots j_n)$, hence

$$|\mathbf{A}|=\Sigma\varepsilon(j_1j_2 \ldots j_n)a_{1j_1}a_{2j_2} \ldots a_{nj_n}.$$

The right-hand side represents the expansion of $|\mathbf{A}'|$, by definition, therefore $|\mathbf{A}|=|\mathbf{A}'|$.

10. In order to be able to use (6) and (7) for the evaluation of determinants, we have to find expressions for the cofactors. Consider first A_{11}. This is the coefficient of a_{11} in (5), thus

$$A_{11}=\Sigma\varepsilon(1i_2 \ldots i_n)a_{i_22} \ldots a_{i_nn},$$

where $i_2 \ldots i_n$ runs over all arrangements of $2 \ldots n$. By E.3, the ε-symbol in this expression is equal to $\varepsilon(i_2 \ldots i_n)$, therefore

$$A_{11}=\Sigma\varepsilon(i_2 \ldots i_n)a_{i_22} \ldots a_{i_nn}.$$

The expression on the right is a determinant of order $n-1$:

$$A_{11}=\begin{vmatrix} a_{22} & a_{23} & \ldots & a_{2n} \\ \cdot & \cdot & \cdots & \cdot \\ a_{n2} & a_{n3} & \ldots & a_{nn} \end{vmatrix}. \tag{8}$$

Thus A_{11} is equal to the $(n-1)$th order determinant which we obtain from $|\mathbf{A}|$ by omitting the first row and the first column. To evaluate A_{ij}, the cofactor of a_{ij}, we move the i-th row up past $\text{row}_{i-1}, \ldots, \text{row}_1$, so that after $i-1$ interchanges it becomes the new top row, and then move the j-th column to the left past the first $j-1$ columns in turn, so that it becomes the initial column. We now have a matrix whose determinant is related to $|\mathbf{A}|$ by $i-1$ interchanges of rows and $j-1$ interchanges of columns; these $i-1+j-1$ interchanges produce

$i+j-2$ changes of sign, or what is the same, $i+j$ changes of sign. Therefore the value of the new determinant is $(-1)^{i+j}|\mathbf{A}|$. The cofactor of a_{ij} in this determinant—in which a_{ij} is now the (1, 1)-element—is the determinant of order $n-1$ obtained from $|\mathbf{A}|$ by omitting the i-th row and j-th column. If we denote this determinant by α_{ij}, we have

$$A_{ij}=(-1)^{i+j}\alpha_{ij}. \tag{9}$$

The $(n-1)$th order determinants α_{ij} are called the *minors* of the determinant $|\mathbf{A}|$, and (9) expresses the cofactors in terms of the minors, the distribution of signs being of the chess-board pattern

$$\begin{vmatrix} + & - & + & - & \cdots \\ - & + & - & + & \cdots \\ + & - & + & - & \cdots \\ & \cdot & \cdot & \cdot & \cdots \end{vmatrix}.$$

11. It is now an easy matter to evaluate determinants. In our first example we use the expansion by the first row:

$$\begin{vmatrix} 7 & 2 & 4 \\ 3 & -4 & 5 \\ 1 & 3 & -2 \end{vmatrix} =7(4.2-3.5)-2(-3.2-5.1)+4(3.3+4.1)=25.$$

If a row or column consists mainly of zeros, it is best to use this in expanding the determinant, e.g.

$$\begin{vmatrix} 3 & 0 & 5 \\ 2 & 0 & 4 \\ 1 & 7 & 3 \end{vmatrix} =(-1)^{3+2}.7.\begin{vmatrix} 3 & 5 \\ 2 & 4 \end{vmatrix} =-14.$$

In particular, the determinant of a 'diagonal matrix'

$$\mathbf{D}=\begin{pmatrix} d_1 & 0 & 0 & \cdots \\ 0 & d_2 & 0 & \cdots \\ \cdot & \cdot & \cdot & \cdots \\ 0 & 0 & 0 & .\,d_n \end{pmatrix},$$

that is, a matrix in which all elements outside the main diagonal[1] are zero, is just the product of the diagonal elements: $|\mathbf{D}|=d_1d_2 \ldots d_n$. This shows that the determinant of the unit-matrix is 1, more generally, for a scalar multiple of the unit-matrix we have $|\lambda\mathbf{I}|=\lambda^n$, where n is the order of the matrix.

In the examples given in ch. II we used the elementary operations α, β, γ to reduce the matrix of a regular system to the unit-matrix. Whenever we carry out such a reduction we can find the value of the determinant at the same time by noting the effect of these operations on the determinant. Thus α—permuting the order of the rows—multiplies the determinant by $+1$ or -1 according as the permutation used was even or odd, β—multiplying a row by a non-zero scalar—multiplies the determinant by that scalar and γ—adding a multiple of one row to another row—leaves the determinant unchanged. At the end of the reduction we have the unit-matrix whose determinant is 1, therefore when we retrace our steps by taking the inverses of the operations α, β, γ used we obtain the determinant of the original matrix. It follows from this that the determinant of a regular matrix cannot be zero. For such a matrix can be reduced to the unit-matrix by operations α, β, γ, and when we evaluate the determinant by applying the inverse operations we obtain for each operation a non-zero factor.

As an illustration we use the matrix of the system discussed in II.9. The operations used were: γ, α (interchange of two rows), β (multiplication by $\frac{1}{2}$), γ, γ, β (multiplication by $\frac{1}{4}$). Hence the determinant is

$$\frac{1}{-1\cdot\frac{1}{2}\cdot\frac{1}{4}}=-8.$$

Of course we can use a reduction after the pattern of ch. II to evaluate any determinant. We apply the operations α, β, γ, noting at each stage the change in the value of the determinant.

[1] The *main diagonal* of a square matrix is the diagonal from the top left-hand corner to the bottom right-hand corner (the diagonal in which the 1's of the unit-matrix stand).

E.g. in the first example of this No., we have

$$\begin{vmatrix} 7 & 2 & 4 \\ 3 & -4 & 5 \\ 1 & 3 & -2 \end{vmatrix} = \begin{vmatrix} 0 & -19 & 18 \\ 0 & -13 & 11 \\ 1 & 3 & -2 \end{vmatrix} = \begin{vmatrix} -19 & 18 \\ -13 & 11 \end{vmatrix} = \begin{vmatrix} -1 & 18 \\ -2 & 11 \end{vmatrix} = \begin{vmatrix} -1 & 18 \\ 0 & -25 \end{vmatrix} = 25.$$

The process of systematically reducing all but one of the elements of a given column (or row) to zero by adding multiples of a fixed row (or column) to the others is called *pivotal condensation*, the unreduced element being the *pivot*. Usually it is convenient, either by division or by taking a combination of rows (or columns), to reduce the pivot to 1. We give a further example (the pivot at each stage is indicated by an asterisk):

$$\begin{vmatrix} 2^* & 6 & -2 & 4 \\ -1 & -2 & 1 & 0 \\ 7 & 13 & 5 & 9 \\ 4 & 8 & -6 & 11 \end{vmatrix} = \begin{vmatrix} 2 & 0 & 0 & 0 \\ -1 & 1 & 0 & 2 \\ 7 & -8 & 12 & -5 \\ 4 & -4 & -2 & 3 \end{vmatrix} = 2\begin{vmatrix} 1^* & 0 & 2 \\ -8 & 12 & -5 \\ -4 & -2 & 3 \end{vmatrix}$$

$$= 2\begin{vmatrix} 1 & 0 & 0 \\ -8 & 12 & 11 \\ -4 & -2 & 11 \end{vmatrix} = 2\begin{vmatrix} 12 & 11 \\ -2 & 11 \end{vmatrix} = 2.11\begin{vmatrix} 12 & 1 \\ -2 & 1 \end{vmatrix} = 2.11.14 = 308.$$

12. If $\mathbf{A}$ is a regular matrix, so that its inverse $\mathbf{A}^{-1}$ exists, we can express this inverse in terms of the determinant and cofactors of $\mathbf{A}$ as follows. We first form the transpose of the matrix of cofactors:

$$\begin{pmatrix} A_{11} & A_{21} & \dots & A_{n1} \\ A_{12} & A_{22} & \dots & A_{n2} \\ \cdot & \cdot & \cdots & \cdot \\ A_{1n} & A_{2n} & \dots & A_{nn} \end{pmatrix}.$$

This matrix is denoted by adj($\mathbf{A}$) and is called the *adjoint* of $\mathbf{A}$, or *adjugate matrix* of $\mathbf{A}$. Now let us evaluate the product $\mathbf{A}$.adj($\mathbf{A}$), for any square matrix $\mathbf{A}$. The (1,1)-element is

$$a_{11}A_{11}+a_{12}A_{12}+ \dots +a_{1n}A_{1n},$$

which equals $|\mathbf{A}|$, by (7). Similarly (7) shows that every element on the main diagonal has the value $|\mathbf{A}|$. Next consider the (2,1)-element

$$a_{21}A_{11}+a_{22}A_{12}+\ldots+a_{2n}A_{1n}.$$

This represents the expansion by the first row of the determinant

$$\begin{vmatrix} a_{21} & a_{22} & \ldots & a_{2n} \\ a_{21} & a_{22} & \ldots & a_{2n} \\ a_{31} & a_{32} & \ldots & a_{3n} \\ \cdot & \cdot & \ldots & \cdot \\ a_{n1} & a_{n2} & \ldots & a_{nn} \end{vmatrix}$$

which has the same 2nd, 3rd, . . . , n-th row as $|\mathbf{A}|$ (because the cofactors A_{11}, A_{12}, . . . , A_{1n} involve only elements from these rows), but its first row is equal to its second row and so its value is zero, by D.2′. Generally,

$$a_{i1}A_{j1}+a_{i2}A_{2j}+\ldots+a_{in}A_{jn}$$

represents the expansion of a determinant whose j-th row is equal to the i-th row of $|\mathbf{A}|$, and whose k-th row for $k\neq j$ is equal to the k-th row of $|\mathbf{A}|$. Hence if $i\neq j$, the i-th and j-th rows in this determinant are the same and its value is zero. Thus the elements on the main diagonal of $\mathbf{A}.\text{adj}(\mathbf{A})$ are $|\mathbf{A}|$ and all other elements are zero; in other words, it is a scalar multiple of the unit-matrix:

$$\mathbf{A}.\text{adj}(\mathbf{A})=|\mathbf{A}|.\mathbf{I}. \qquad (10)$$

Similarly, using (6) for the diagonal elements, and D.2 for the non-diagonal elements, we can prove that

$$\text{adj}(\mathbf{A}).\mathbf{A}=|\mathbf{A}|.\mathbf{I}. \qquad (11)$$

These formulae hold for any square matrix $\mathbf{A}$. Now suppose that $|\mathbf{A}|\neq 0$, and form the matrix

$$\mathbf{B}=\frac{1}{|\mathbf{A}|}\text{adj}(\mathbf{A}).$$

Equations (10) and (11) show that $\mathbf{AB}=\mathbf{BA}=\mathbf{I}$, hence a matrix $\mathbf{A}$ whose determinant is $\neq 0$ is regular and its inverse is given by

$$\mathbf{A}^{-1}=\frac{1}{|\mathbf{A}|}\operatorname{adj}(\mathbf{A}). \tag{12}$$

Conversely, as we saw in No. 11, a regular matrix has a non-zero determinant. Hence we may say that

A square matrix $\mathbf{A}$ *is regular if and only if* $|\mathbf{A}|\neq 0$.

In other words, the vanishing of $|\mathbf{A}|$ is a necessary and sufficient condition for the linear dependence of the columns of $\mathbf{A}$, so that the determinant provides a numerical criterion for the linear independence of vectors.

13. The formula (12) for the inverse matrix may also be used to obtain an explicit expression for the solution of a regular system of equations. By (12), the solution of

$$\mathbf{A}\mathbf{x}=\mathbf{k} \tag{13}$$

is

$$\mathbf{x}=\mathbf{A}^{-1}\mathbf{k}=\frac{1}{|\mathbf{A}|}\operatorname{adj}(\mathbf{A})\mathbf{k},$$

i.e.

$$x_i=\frac{1}{|\mathbf{A}|}(A_{1i}k_1+A_{2i}k_2+\ldots+A_{ni}k_n).$$

The bracket on the right represents the expansion, by the i-th column, of the determinant of the matrix

$$\mathbf{A}^{(i)}=(\mathbf{a}_1,\ldots,\mathbf{a}_{i-1},\mathbf{k},\mathbf{a}_{i+1},\ldots,\mathbf{a}_n), \tag{14}$$

which is obtained when the i-th column of $\mathbf{A}$ is replaced by $\mathbf{k}$. Hence the solution of (13) may be written as a quotient of two determinants thus:

$$x_i=\frac{|\mathbf{A}^{(i)}|}{|\mathbf{A}|} \qquad (i=1,\ldots,n), \tag{15}$$

where the matrix $\mathbf{A}^{(i)}$ is defined by (14). This formula for solving a regular system of equations is known as *Cramer's Rule.*

14. A further important property of determinants, the multi-

plication theorem, states that if **A**, **B** are two $n \times n$ matrices, then the determinant of their product equals the product of their determinants:

$$|\mathbf{AB}| = |\mathbf{A}| . |\mathbf{B}|. \tag{16}$$

We shall give a proof[1] which illustrates the use of Cramer's Rule.

Firstly we note that both sides of (16) are polynomials in the $2n^2$ elements of **A** and **B**. If we regard these elements as variables, then the determinants $|\mathbf{A}|$, $|\mathbf{B}|$, $|\mathbf{AB}|$ are not zero,[2] and we may therefore assume **A**, **B** and **AB** to be regular in what follows.

The system $\mathbf{Bx} = \mathbf{k}$ has a unique solution, which by Cramer's Rule, may be written

$$x_i = \frac{|\mathbf{B}^{(i)}|}{|\mathbf{B}|},$$

where $\mathbf{B}^{(i)} = (\mathbf{b}_1, \ldots, \mathbf{b}_{i-1}, \mathbf{k}, \mathbf{b}_{i+1}, \ldots, \mathbf{b}_n)$. Here $\mathbf{b}_1, \ldots, \mathbf{b}_n$ are the columns of **B**, so that $\mathbf{B}^{(i)}$ does not involve the i-th column of **B**. Now the solution of $\mathbf{Bx} = \mathbf{k}$ plainly also satisfies the equation

$$\mathbf{ABx} = \mathbf{Ak},$$

and the solution of this system is, again by Cramer's Rule,

$$x_i = \frac{|\mathbf{AB}^{(i)}|}{|\mathbf{AB}|},$$

where
$$\begin{aligned}\mathbf{AB}^{(i)} &= \mathbf{A}(\mathbf{b}_1, \ldots, \mathbf{b}_{i-1}, \mathbf{k}, \mathbf{b}_{i+1}, \ldots, \mathbf{b}_n) \\ &= (\mathbf{Ab}_1, \ldots, \mathbf{Ab}_{i-1}, \mathbf{Ak}, \mathbf{Ab}_{i+1}, \ldots, \mathbf{Ab}_n)\end{aligned}$$

(cf. ch. III, ex. 6). Since the solution is the same in each case, we have

$$\frac{|\mathbf{B}^{(i)}|}{|\mathbf{B}|} = \frac{|\mathbf{AB}^{(i)}|}{|\mathbf{AB}|} \qquad (i = 1, \ldots, n),$$

and hence[3]

$$\frac{|\mathbf{AB}|}{|\mathbf{B}|} = \frac{|\mathbf{AB}^{(i)}|}{|\mathbf{B}^{(i)}|} \qquad (i = 1, \ldots, n). \tag{17}$$

In this equation the right-hand side does not involve the i-th

[1] Due to Kronecker.

[2] These determinants do not vanish identically as functions of the $2n^2$ variables, since they are $\neq 0$ for $\mathbf{A} = \mathbf{B} = \mathbf{I}$.

[3] If the components of the vector **k** are again taken as variables, neither the numerator nor the denominator of the right-hand side of (17) vanishes.

column of **B**, therefore neither does the left-hand side. Since this holds for $i=1, \ldots, n$, $|\mathbf{AB}|/|\mathbf{B}|$ is independent of **B** altogether and we may evaluate it by giving **B** any particular value, e.g. $\mathbf{B}=\mathbf{I}$:

$$\frac{|\mathbf{AB}|}{|\mathbf{B}|}=\frac{|\mathbf{A}|}{|\mathbf{I}|}=|\mathbf{A}|.$$

Multiplying up, we find that $|\mathbf{AB}|=|\mathbf{A}||\mathbf{B}|$, i.e. (16).

15. The linear dependence of r vectors of dimension n can be characterized as follows by means of determinants. We know already that a linearly independent set of n-vectors contains at most n vectors (Theorem 2, II.10), so we may suppose $r \leqslant n$. From the components of these r vectors we can form a determinant of order r by choosing any r rows. In this way we obtain $\binom{n}{r}=\frac{n!}{(n-r)!r!}$ determinants of order r.

The vanishing of these $\binom{n}{r}$ *determinants is necessary and sufficient for the linear dependence of the r vectors.*

Thus, e.g., the vectors $\mathbf{u}=(u_1, u_2, u_3)'$, $\mathbf{v}=(v_1, v_2, v_3)'$ are linearly dependent if and only if

$$\begin{vmatrix} u_2 & v_2 \\ u_3 & v_3 \end{vmatrix} = \begin{vmatrix} u_1 & v_1 \\ u_3 & v_3 \end{vmatrix} = \begin{vmatrix} u_1 & v_1 \\ u_2 & v_2 \end{vmatrix} = 0.$$ [1]

To prove the assertion, let $\mathbf{u}_1, \ldots, \mathbf{u}_r$ be linearly dependent vectors in n dimensions, say

$$\mathbf{u}_1=\lambda_2\mathbf{u}_2+\ldots+\lambda_r\mathbf{u}_r.$$

Then in any determinant formed by taking r rows of the $n \times r$ matrix $(\mathbf{u}_1, \ldots, \mathbf{u}_r)$, we can make the first column zero by subtracting $\lambda_2\text{col}_2+\ldots+\lambda_r\text{col}_r$. Hence these determinants all vanish.

For the converse suppose that the r vectors $\mathbf{u}_1, \ldots, \mathbf{u}_r$ are linearly independent, and consider the n rows of the $n \times r$ matrix $(\mathbf{u}_1, \ldots, \mathbf{u}_r)$. Let s be the maximum number of linearly independent rows; to complete the proof we need only show that $s=r$, for

[1] Geometrically this means that two vectors in space are linearly dependent if and only if their projections on the three coordinate planes are linearly dependent.

then there exist r rows with a non-vanishing determinant. We may suppose the rows so numbered that the first s are linearly independent, while the remaining $n-s$ rows depend on them. This means that the vector equation

$$\mathbf{u}_1x_1 + \ldots + \mathbf{u}_rx_r = \mathbf{0} \tag{18}$$

is equivalent to the scalar equations

$$\begin{aligned} u_{11}x_1 + \ldots + u_{1r}x_r &= 0 \\ \cdot \quad \cdot \quad \cdots \quad & \cdot \quad \cdot \\ u_{s1}x_1 + \ldots + u_{sr}x_r &= 0, \end{aligned} \tag{19}$$

where $u_{1i}, u_{2i}, \ldots, u_{ni}$ are the components of $\mathbf{u}_i$. Since the rows have r components, a linearly independent set of rows can have at most r elements (Theorem 2, II.10), and so $s \leqslant r$. If we had $s < r$, then the system (19) would have more than s columns, and these columns would therefore be linearly dependent. This means that (19) would have a non-trivial solution, and so would (18), because it is equivalent to (19). But this contradicts the linear independence of $\mathbf{u}_1, \ldots, \mathbf{u}_r$. Hence $s = r$, and the determinant of the system (19) provides a non-zero determinant of order r.

16. To describe the rank of an $m \times n$ matrix $\mathbf{A}$ we consider the determinants which can be formed from $\mathbf{A}$ by omitting from $\mathbf{A}$ all but k rows and k columns. Such a determinant will be called a *minor*[1] *of order k*. E.g. the matrix

$$\begin{vmatrix} a_1 & a_2 & a_3 \\ b_1 & b_2 & b_3 \end{vmatrix}$$

has 6 first order minors: a_i, b_i ($i = 1, 2, 3$) and 3 second order minors, obtained by omitting each of the 3 columns in turn.

If $\mathbf{A}$ has rank r, then we can, by the result of No. 15, choose a non-zero minor of order r. And if $\mathbf{A}$ contains a non-zero minor of order s, then the s columns which go to make up this minor are linearly independent (again by the result of No. 15), so that the rank is at least s in this case. Hence the rank may be characterized as follows:

The rank of a matrix $\mathbf{A}$ *is the greatest number r such that* $\mathbf{A}$ *contains a non-vanishing minor of order r.*

[1] In this terminology the minors of an $n \times n$ matrix introduced previously become 'minors of order $n-1$'.

Since the determinant of a (square) matrix equals the determinant of its transpose, a matrix contains non-zero minors of a given order k if and only if its transpose contains non-zero minors of order k. It follows that the rank of any matrix (not necessarily square) equals the rank of its transpose. In other words, a matrix has as many linearly independent rows as it has linearly independent columns. Applied to systems of equations this means that a system of rank r has just r (and no more) equations whose left-hand sides are linearly independent. This result is already implicit in the process of solving homogeneous systems of equations described in IV.6–7, where we found that any system of rank r could be reduced to an equivalent system consisting of r equations, which were linearly independent, because each served for the determination of a different unknown in terms of the $n-r$ disposable unknowns.

EXERCISES ON CHAPTER V

1. Evaluate: (i) $\varepsilon(14532)$, (ii) $\varepsilon(41532)$, (iii) $\varepsilon(14325)$, (iv) $\varepsilon(521436)$, (v) $\varepsilon(5314762)$, (vi) $\varepsilon(231)$, (vii) $\varepsilon(2341)$, (viii) $\varepsilon(23451)$, (ix) $\varepsilon(321)$, (x) $\varepsilon(4321)$, (xi) $\varepsilon(54321)$, (xii) $\varepsilon(654321)$.

2. Find the determinants of the matrices occurring in ex. 1, ch. II.

3. Show that the determinant of a 'triangular' matrix corresponding to a system as in ex. 2, ch. II, is equal to the product of the elements on the main diagonal.

4. Test the linear dependence of the sets of vectors in ex. 2, ch. I, by finding non-zero determinants of maximal order formed from their components.

5. Determine the ranks of the systems in ex. 9, ch. IV, by using determinants.

6. Evaluate

(i) $\begin{vmatrix} 1 & 3 & 2 \\ 8 & 4 & 0 \\ 2 & 1 & 2 \end{vmatrix}$ (ii) $\begin{vmatrix} 6 & 5 & 2 \\ 3 & 0 & -1 \\ -7 & 2 & 4 \end{vmatrix}$ (iii) $\begin{vmatrix} 1 & -2 & -3 & 4 \\ -2 & 3 & 4 & -5 \\ 3 & -4 & -5 & 6 \\ -4 & 5 & 6 & -7 \end{vmatrix}$

(iv) $\begin{vmatrix} 1 & 1 & 1 & -1 \\ 1 & 1 & -1 & 1 \\ 1 & -1 & 1 & 1 \\ -1 & 1 & 1 & 1 \end{vmatrix}$ (v) $\begin{vmatrix} 3 & 9 & 27 & 81 \\ 1 & 1 & 1 & 1 \\ -2 & 4 & -8 & 16 \\ 2 & 4 & 8 & 16 \end{vmatrix}$.

7. Evaluate

(i) $\begin{vmatrix} 1 & 1 & 1 & 1 \\ a & b & c & d \\ a^2 & b^2 & c^2 & d^2 \\ a^3 & b^3 & c^3 & d^3 \end{vmatrix}$ (ii) $\begin{vmatrix} a & b & c & d \\ a^2 & b^2 & c^2 & d^2 \\ a^3 & b^3 & c^3 & d^3 \\ a^4 & b^4 & c^4 & d^4 \end{vmatrix}$

(iii) $\begin{vmatrix} 1 & 1 & 1 & 1 \\ a & b & c & d \\ a^2 & b^2 & c^2 & d^2 \\ a^4 & b^4 & c^4 & d^4 \end{vmatrix}$ (iv) $\begin{vmatrix} 0 & a & b & c \\ -a & 0 & d & e \\ -b & -d & 0 & f \\ -c & -e & -f & 0 \end{vmatrix}$.

8. Determine the rank of the following matrices, for all values of t:

(i) $\begin{pmatrix} 3 & 1 & -2 & 4 \\ 6 & 2 & t & 8 \\ 0 & t & 0 & 0 \end{pmatrix}$ (ii) $\begin{pmatrix} t & 1 & 0 \\ 0 & t & 0 \\ 0 & 0 & t+3 \end{pmatrix}$

(iii) $\begin{pmatrix} 3 & 0 & 6 & 3t \\ t & 2 & 2(t+1) & 0 \\ -2 & 4 & 0 & -2t-2t^2 \end{pmatrix}$.

9. The vector product of two 3-vectors **u**, **v** is defined as the vector $\mathbf{w}=(u_2v_3-u_3v_2, u_3v_1-u_1v_3, u_1v_2-u_2v_1)$. Show that the components of **w** may be written

$$w_i=\sum \varepsilon(ijk)u_jv_k,$$

where the summation is over the permutations of 123 which have i in the first place, and that **w** is zero if and only if **u** and **v** are linearly dependent.

10. If **A** is a regular matrix of order n, then $|adj(\mathbf{A})| = |\mathbf{A}|^{n-1}$. (This result is true for any square matrix, regular or not.)

11. Use the multiplication theorem of determinants to give a direct proof of the fact that a matrix which has an inverse has a non-zero determinant.

ANSWERS TO THE EXERCISES

I. 2. (ii), (iii), (iv). 4. The points represented by the vectors are not collinear with the origin. 6. A basis is given by (0, 1, 0, 0), (0, 0, 1, 1).

II. 1. (The solution is written as a row-vector in each case):
(i) (2, −1, 5), (ii) (−3, 1, 0), (iii) (4, −2, 1), (iv) (26, 5, −11·4), (v) (0, 0, 0), (vi) (1·5, 1, −1, 2), (vii) (5, −1, −2, 1), (viii) (−208, −141, −9, 13).

III. 2. (*a*) (i) (ii) (iii) (iv), (*b*) (i) (iii) (iv), (*c*) (iii). 3. $\mathbf{A}^2 - \mathbf{AB} - \mathbf{BA} + \mathbf{B}^2$. 4. $\begin{pmatrix} a & b \\ \dfrac{-a^2}{b} & -a \end{pmatrix}$ (for all a, b subject to $b \neq 0$) and $\begin{pmatrix} 0 & 0 \\ c & 0 \end{pmatrix}$ (for all c). 5. $\mathbf{A}^2 = \begin{pmatrix} -11 & -15 \\ 9 & -14 \end{pmatrix}$, $\mathbf{A}^2 - 3\mathbf{A} + 17\mathbf{I} = \mathbf{O}$.

8.
$$\mathbf{uu}' = \begin{pmatrix} 9 & -6 & 3 & 12 \\ -6 & 4 & -2 & -8 \\ 3 & -2 & 1 & 4 \\ 12 & -8 & 4 & 16 \end{pmatrix} \quad \mathbf{u}'\mathbf{u} = (30).$$

IV. 1. (i) $\begin{pmatrix} -2 & -1 & 3 \\ 1 & 0 & -1 \\ 1 & 2 & -2 \end{pmatrix}$ (ii) $\dfrac{1}{60}\begin{pmatrix} -14 & 55 & 80 \\ 10 & -35 & -40 \\ 2 & -25 & -20 \end{pmatrix}$

(iii) $\dfrac{1}{6}\begin{pmatrix} 20 & -1 & -12 \\ -9 & 3 & 3 \\ 2 & -1 & 0 \end{pmatrix}$ (iv) $\begin{pmatrix} 5·5 & 9·5 & -5 \\ 1 & 2 & -1 \\ -2·5 & -4·5 & 2·4 \end{pmatrix}$

(v) $\frac{1}{2}\begin{pmatrix} 7 & -2 & 17 \\ -6 & 2 & -16 \\ 7 & -2 & 19 \end{pmatrix}$ (vi) $\frac{1}{8}\begin{pmatrix} 26 & 1 & -17 & -30 \\ -72 & 0 & 40 & 64 \\ -4 & -2 & 10 & 20 \\ -36 & -2 & 26 & 44 \end{pmatrix}$

(vii) $\frac{1}{6}\begin{pmatrix} 3 & 3 & 4 & -14 \\ 0 & 6 & 0 & 30 \\ 0 & 0 & -2 & 4 \\ 0 & 0 & 0 & 6 \end{pmatrix}$ (viii) $\frac{1}{4}\begin{pmatrix} 66 & -140 & -64 & 8 \\ 43 & -92 & -44 & 4 \\ 1 & -4 & -4 & 0 \\ -4 & 8 & 4 & 0 \end{pmatrix}$

5. 0 or 1. 9. (i) $\frac{1}{2}(-1, 1, 0)+\lambda(5, -3, 2)$, (ii) $\lambda(-14, 11, 16)$ (iii) no solution, (iv) $(2, -1, 1, 0)+\lambda(12, 1, -20, 7)$, (v) $(0, 1, -1, 1)+\lambda(1, -3, 0, 0)$, (vi) $(0, 0, 1, 1)$, (vii) $(1, 0, 0, 0)+\lambda(-1, 1, 1, 0)+\mu(-2, 2, 0, 1)$. 10. (i) $t=6$: $\frac{1}{7}(-10, 13, 0, 0)+\lambda(-10, 6, 7, 0)+\mu(1, -1, 0, 1)$, (ii) $t=1$: $(0, 1, 0, 0)+\lambda(-2, 0, 1, 0)+\mu(-2, 1, 0, 1)$, $t=-\frac{2}{5}$: $\frac{1}{25}(21, -17, 0, 0)+\lambda(-2, 0, 1, 0)+\mu(-2, 1, 0, 1)$, (iii) $t=5$: $\lambda(5, 1, -4)$.

N.B. The solutions to questions 9 and 10 can take different forms, depending on the choice of the particular solution and the basis for the solution of the associated homogeneous system.

V. 1. (i) -1, (ii) 1, (iii) -1, (iv) 1, (v) 1, (vi) 1, (vii) -1, (viii) 1, (ix) -1, (x) 1, (xi) 1, (xii) -1. 2. (i) 1, (ii) -60, (iii) 12, (iv) 10, (v) 2, (vi) -8, (vii) -6, (viii) 4. 5. (i) 2, (ii) 2, (iii) 2, (iv) 3, (v) 3, (vi) 4, (vii) 2. 6. (i) -40, (ii) -1, (iii) 0, (iv) -16, (v) -1440. 7. (i) Δ, (ii) $abcd\Delta$, (iii) $(a+b+c+d)\Delta$, where $\Delta=(d-c)(d-b)(d-a)(c-b)(c-a)(b-a)$, (iv) $(af-be+cd)^2$. 8. (i) The rank is 2 if $t=0$ or -4, and 3 otherwise, (ii) the rank is 2 if $t=0$ or -3, and 3 otherwise, (iii) the rank is 2 for all t.

Index